PROTOTYPI

(2020)

CONTENTS

)

Emily Critchley

–

Tonight

for Marianne Morris

Everything is a part of everything that is a part of everything else.
And any decision is like a huge moon
tossed from the top of a great hill. It gathers speed
in direct proportion to height,
taking each prisoner down with it.
It and the tides.

And when we were younger, things dropped
were as stones into that ocean. But now,
just as the moon gapes, we have run out
of ideas.

(Everything is a part of everything else
that is a part of nothing.
The moon moves; cuts its teeth
on our regretful actions. Like that time
we made bombs out of love.
Live bombs sent to rip us with.
And she grew, O,
into a strong one.

But look, if you still see the moon
–above–
craning her neck for a better view (it is what
I drew)
there must be some hope then.

(from *Home*)

Helen Marten

–

Messrs. External and Earthly
The Somebody Logo

We cannot remember much of our origins. Namely only a jumble
of things, of objects past: hands emptying jars with an economy of
movement, touching indulgences in drawers, avoiding the drunkard
papers slow with small print, the dapple-bellied plates all old jam
and crumbs, whole chicken in one pot, coarse hairs and the pleasure
of self-love beneath the covers. We had a knack for the resuscitative
energies of matter. How the bloated belly of the cathode TV on one
mother's counter quite merrily matched the lens of another covetous
eye and its dilation over bright squares of clothing on the neighbour's
line. Things not to be assessed by their own causality for our feelings
are indigenous to place.

   There are so many things we want to tell. But perhaps we have
forgotten. How to conjugate the verbs to describe varicose veins and
the dull defective clunk of bedsores or bunions. We've forgotten or   )
never knew the celestial essence of industrial psychology, and why the
hot sweet gush of milk before bed does something thick and rich to our
bodies' proteins to make us sleep well. And isn't that nice, because out
there with the counted sheep and the zzz's it's possible to breathe into
one another, to feel unfixed and light not dead with heavy kidneys and
a flooded heart.

   There is one way to start – with the furniture – worth noting the
degree of polish, the certain grade of skill in turns around the legs.
Or start by flinging out a voice, by sticking your fingers in the sockets,
bumping into walls as someone falls down the stairs just trying to
orient up from down. Wet shoes. Somewhere thereabouts lie all the
beginnings that happen and end, cryptic and forlorn, blowing about in
the lawless territory between fact and fiction.

   There's always one set of hands – or many – fiddling with laces
only to come up holding weeds that scorch a rash across the palms.
Just tying shoes to move along. And often, because it's rained in this
country as it always does, there's a sudden consciousness of having

feet, having *wet feet* on *wet sod* that mutually weep beneath us. Having feet being a symptom of self that gets you back to basics. Gets you moving again.

Learn to deal with it, families used to say. *There'll be much turning,* they said, and how was anyone to fathom what was meant by that? Were we complicit or affected? To nod our heads endlessly with theirs, those nods constructed upon the very absence of affirmation and us moving our thick skulls up and down only to avoid words or keep warm or busy? Was it to be *that* kind of turning?

We knew that weaving through the rocky diagram of living, above oozing noodles of worms and tree roots, under blown glass skies, just looking for where you came from, was only one part of the bitter progress. But we didn't know the complications. That the where you came from and the where you belong might change with every limping day. All the moves in the world, forward and back, seemed told in a poor broken semaphore performed half from memory and the rest signed out with only mildly burning twigs so the general rhythm of instruction was first confused then ultimately collapsed. We lost our category.

(

Remember the wise maternal function of family? The good and bad objects, the nurses and lovers, the crumbs and morsels, pools and positions of speech and support? People are simply a collection of individuals shaken and salted, sometimes strapped uncomfortably together. Everyone performs their dynamic process of labour: they judge and are judged. The audience has always been a point of reference against which theatre defines itself.

Some folk might tilt their chins and say *there are no stones in the sky, so no stones can fall from the sky!* We disagree. Each infant arriving in this world makes its entrance in a rush of wind. The child breaks things and then things break the child. Sometimes wind arrives like a rodent thought and knocks you hard about the head, shatters an alphabet of new feeling inside your skull. Cars accelerate, bones are broken, soda belched and blown away. Stick your tongue out in a thin haze of rain and you taste the ash of the city, its fried fish, its petrol, its joints rolled up and spat hot in burning greens back out into the air.

This is the circulation of circulation itself. A breathing set of people and their places. Some wind singles you out. From the first flicker of a leaf you know it points directly at you. It says your name and spoils poetry with reason and conjecture. When you are touched by wind, by the forces that bend the trees and scatter dirt hard and fast against windows, this is communication. We tend to underestimate the power of wind. We are something of all these flickers: not individual listeners in any front row or figures red faced on a stage, but rather the soft mist of expectancy that settles slowly about the ears and refuses not to be heard.

We are the Messrs. The instruments of psychic observation. We are not the moral function of behaviour, neither analyst nor pulse. We are spectator, servant and clown. We are animal, vegetable, mineral. Our flight takes us everywhere. We are interested. We see broken men and women, and cast the spaces in between. We found these two, Ethan and Patrice, and bedded down to watch them squeal.

)

There is Ethan. The King of beers and chicken fingers. His beard is desiccated, meaning passions take weeks to grow through secrets and skin. There is Patrice. The Queen of hearts and ripping them out. Her fingers are cut and have bled down into the soil. They eat at the table of what they have left unfinished. They are amazed individuals in skirts and shorts, rolling their shoes over curb stones, gravel in their soles. Their thoughts are of bed and warm socks, not the absurd dirt of other people. The abstracts of other people. They are bodies in need of chemically better living. They don't reveal their focus is money, they tell you they're after happiness. They are silhouettes to follow and unfold. They are full of blood, which alongside other people always acts thick like a thief. It understands itself as a molecule amidst structure. It is hands in the kitchen, peat on the riverbank. It is rubber on the asphalt and any number of cosmologies under the nail. It sets down its load in the veins of cats and the boxes of storage centres. If the critics are staggered with definition, spare a thought for the people. The awkward and virginal people, when it comes to facts.

So show us a house, we'll draw you mustard nags panting.
Show us a barn, we'll tell you a myth.
Show us a tent, we'll assess the erotics of its pitch.
We Messrs. after all, are busy setting a tilt.

(

(from *The Boiled in Between*)

Lavinia Singer

–

Cave

is
  no thing
  but light
      play
articulating stone
  the strike & pick
strung
between
  no thing
  but air
pressed in each rift
  lift & drop
     handling
as the world
      tilts
  [tide turn]
surfaces   )
  shiver
  in conversation
& masses
    dissolve to
  no thing
  but water
     clear
  bled from the
    bay's arm
drift-wood
     adds to
  the vocabulary
    of forms
 for what else
    does
 the soundless
  base speak
    in the dark
    dark

after *Sculpture with Colour (Deep Blue and Red) [6]*, Barbara Hepworth   9

Between Spaces

the built, not-built and inbetween | lost, or what never were | oases of ornament | off-the-scale with a racked-up bill | *where the moon king rides ever under moonlight* | banking crisis | scarcity of funds | debt | doubt | disputed territories | political indelicacies | the death of the architect | temporarily 'put on hold' | *my client is not in a hurry* | high stress | pressure points | the movement of what should never move | collapsing mathematics | where flights of fancy meet design flaws | *its parts ballooned like sugar loaves!* | unimaginable | it takes the breath away | [pause] | youthful optimism | or else, illogic | hurricanes | flooding | subsidence | plague-pit | excavated skulls | test-site | set-back | war | exuberant graffiti on a concrete shell | informal communities | differences of opinion | disrepair | a shake of hands | change of hands | sleight of hands | vanished | under the canopy of heaven | morning breaks

(

Soaring Flight

The sea is mood

    it edges the vision
                         field
    with its blue
        not blue
            so how will I be held

Greenscape
      mass
            pouring

the coast I gasp
           entangled in
      air
thrusts
      & backing
      wind

Up here   )
      I'm bucked

drift hitting
sky-blocks

         Shift
      to the stall
            turn
red route home

      thinned now

nosing
      for

       call it

      loss

Caleb Klaces

—

Middlemarch

Amir kneels to watch a shoal pass through another shoal.
Jamila asks her companions the name of the waiter.
Freya plays 'Brothers in Arms' with her band *Around the Wall*.

Fish nibble rice in Hari's dishwater.
Karl stops his tram for a samba band.
Neil glances at the wing mirror and then at his phone.

Caleb hurries through the uneven scrubland.
Oraib convinces the family not to return home.
Basak mops up sauce from her mother's plate.

At the orphanage Xavier greets the new children.
Dusan looks in the box to find a good net.
Once settled on the train Qiu eats a steamed bun.

(

Rael's friend is upset and Rael holds his friend's hand.
Seunghwan sings and rolls over in her sleep.
Gabriel spends some time checking on the odd sound.

Mingmar looks for caterpillar fungus on the slope.
Thea chews in time with the music.
Valerie sucks a mint with her eyes on the stars.

Pierre hops towards his other sock.
Udu rubs his big toe while he says his prayers.
Ivan opens the plug of his sewing machine.

Yesenia tucks a stranger into her own bed.
Eray starts the car and leaves it running.
Wasilei laughs because his leg has gone dead.

Lara enters the stage and unbuttons her gown.
Zhanna giggles while she pretends to frown.

IKT-SVO

The sun rolls into the chest of the vending machine. Dusk tumbles off the shelf.
Four billion chickens close their eyes and dream of dreaming. Tucked under

the advancing shade, bodies lie down, row upon row, sinking deep into the mosses
growing in the corners of the server. Everywhere the earthworms return once again

to their volume on the afterlife. Notions of proximity and distance, above and below,
in front and behind, cease to be altogether precise. A cosmonaut, whom Gorbachev

had sent up to Mir, still a Soviet citizen, falls in Kazakhstan *as if to a foreign land*.
Perched in the nest that hangs from my father's chin, I look down at a small child

with no shadows to speak of on my entire body and I laugh. The door swings open
and the shopping arrives. The household insects chuckle in the less obvious machinery.

Then it became apparent that it was not because we were laughing that the house
was falling down. There was a hurricane. A swollen purple face bubbled up from the   )

broadband. Here comes the sun. Only five billion years to wait now. I find
myself tumbling out of the sky. I meet my reflection with a gentle splash.

As it lumbers over the horizon, plants send their roots deep in search of nutrients,
cracking rocks. Domestic canines hear the gentle grinding noise as the darkness

is shelved and the people rise, struck by the will to stand. The plane lands the same
time it departed. Four billion chickens open their eyes and dream of dreaming.

(from *My Little Finger*)   13

Ali Lewis

–

Break-up Poem for Half-Homeland

You are a huge rock I want to put down
but the floor is newly-hatched ducklings.

There are two kinds of bottomless
champagne flutes and you are the worse kind.
I carry you around from room to room,
appalling people.

I don't want to be a sadness evangelist,
but that clip of a cat
with its head in a bag
it can't back out of —
it reminds me this:

(that time we tried on the headsets
and played virtual reality *Rollercoaster Sim*,

how we found at last
what we couldn't look away from
and it made us all sick.

I'm a Failure. Born with a Wooden Spoon in My Mouth.

Why are people like they are when they could easily not be.
Take me (please!) — I'm nothing like me and I've not been
for years. I don't even remember the get-up I came with.
I think I liked bands. I think I cleaned my ears with the arms
of my glasses. Actors. That's what we are (yes since you ask
I've trod a few boards I've lit a few limes). Here's my advice.
Line up your possibilities: it's shoeshine night and new school
tomorrow. When an actor's on stage they've got to be both
convincing and loud but they're not the same thing. Once
I got such good tickets I could see the actors' actual faces,
but they were doing these massive emotions for the guys
in the back and honestly it was all a bit much. They should range
audiences in order of vision. That way the young would be up
in the gods and the super old rich people would get the stalls.
Wait. Guys you could do this yourself. You're already doing it.
Hey! Look at you acting. Pretending your ice-cream tastes not
like flat wooden spoon (which remember? is what losers get).   )
Here's my impression of you figuring it out: Jesus, who writes
this shit? Me? That doesn't make sense. Wouldn't I have cared
more? Wouldn't I have written me a little more likeable?

Aisha Farr

–

Here is a solid block of wood

Here is a man
who has a solid block of wood
of the largest size. It is outside of himself,
lying in front of him, while within himself
he has the intention and skill to make
an image of the smallest size
from that part of the wood
which, measured by plumb line,
lies in the centre
and middle of the block.

The nape of the boy's neck is most easy to love. Is it pathetic to take
pleasure in male vulnerability? This should be rephrased as an issue
of surfaces: the soft bareness of the back of the boy's neck is a visual
experience which anticipates touch. And so, how easily a knife would
slide into this mental image as a means of exploring doubt within thought.

I heard
a man say that he made a knife with which to cut fruit.
If it's used, he said, *to cut other things that's not my fault.*
I heard
a woman mention guilt but not know what else to say;
the word
a stand-in for what she couldn't say because
the word
was standing in the way.

While the block is still
completely whole, the image may exist inside
himself through the sheer power of imagination,
but common sense tells you that before he can
manage to see it clearly with the bodily sight of his
outward eyes, or reveal it to be seen by others, he

(

must always use his skill and his tools to remove
all the outward parts of the wood that surround
the image and prevent it from being seen. This
lies contrary to what nature illustrates.

The colour of him is ash, which is only a strange coincidence.
He is familiar as a recurring thought, inherited perspective.
You imagine your face as the hole he wanted to be buried in,
expressionless as a basking shark, rounding to the peg.
Choosing a colour to describe him
gets closest to how far you are.
A warm pillar you can put your arms around, he is also a soothing
height. You're breakable as a pact. Putting your arms around
him
also restricts your view. Perhaps desire and fear are just two names
for the same thing. One pillar doesn't make an edifice structurally sound,
and soundness isn't always the best way to hear. You can't only be measurable
to yourself by drawing a line around the bit he *didn't* see now can you.

)

Face

Not really. The face I drew in
the untouched sand on the
beach. Leaving something
there so I could take it with
me. It is a reliquary for my
images, borrowed thing to say,
I am myself at everything. It's
in a bad way, a habit you-
plural. Pain felt me

as I dragged a line with my
hands. I liked the way the sand
could only displace, furred at
the edges of what I meant.
Nowhere else to go, for me I
climb the dunes again. From
the top I could see it, so big
now far away. It was my
mother's face as always, each
year mine again. Reach to

touch her face. It is the height
of you your fingers reach its
ends the height it is. Raise
your arms to touch the place
you were born first, where her
brow meets her warm brow,
your palms flat on that bone
plain and buried. She was
made careful too as the x of
treasure

(

in the head. Stroke down her
face's side with your truer
hand 'til crouching at the jaw's
edge you're forced to lie then
sink like tired sea into the
shadow by her neck. A stone
placed obvious next to water
moving in from somewhere.
You can stop now her idea.

)

Grass's sake

It's important that I don't apologise he says.
His eyes are open and he appears to be seeing me.
My horizon is the width of his face, he always was
so wide before me. There are two freckles on his
neck and whatever thinking is I think on them.
The sound of his voice is harder to hear than what
he says. His ear keeps eclipsing the edge of a tree
behind him the bark is so complicated. The whole
of life is doing harm we live by killing the grass under
our bodies as we sit together trying to explain relation.
I know I say how everything gets used within your poems.
The circle of stones you visited with Arts Council Funding,
the friend you fucked and wrote about with Arts Council Funding,
the comparison you made in cleverly-crafted verse between a monument
and the temporary, the moment suspended in which you used a woman like
a man uses a woman to reshape your pain, like a man uses a poem to avoid
with cleverness their pain. Your poems are becoming formulas by which you
can live with yourself I tell him inside the poem. Outside the poem I tell him
about how Penelope came down to the large room full of waiting suitors, the
men who know what they want without knowing who the wanted really is. He
gets the parallel and he circles. He watches me. One suitor has an instrument
and as he plays he sings of a dying man, of the present moment as it happens
at sea. Penelope interrupts to plead he not sing so presently
of something that is still happening as though it's over when
it's not. A friend told me about that. I sit on the grass opposite
him and sense the shape I am before him. I see his one soft pink
eclipsing ear. I anticipate him pointing out Penelope doing her own
un-weaving. If he was writing this the unseen shape of me is the very
shape this poem would be. He can know me only with his small scissors.
Inside the poem he says I think she was just a container for my pain. He's
not looking at me now so I get away with thinking that it should be about
wholeness, all of it. This conclusion is moderate and it looks a mess. Outside
of the poem he tells me he wants to have children. Inside of the poem I reply.
Please stop writing long enough for grass's sake.

(

Alex MacDonald

–

Blank Inside For Your Message

A featureless morning, a supermarket roof
of a day spent thinking in framed sunlight,

bare pages and what the windscreen knows.
Someone sings of entering your world like spring,

and here's a new feeling in the get-go of radio.
Now I'm an iceberg breaking away in bath water

and wow these vacant prairies. What came
before this, moist handshake days

and coming home like an egg-heavy salmon?
Each noble idea segmented leaves a pith

)

and history only returns when fully extinguished,
a thought like a manager in their empty restaurant.

Tuesday's coming with a dirge knotted in its heart
but oh! these are the tiara wearing days my friends,

the long-sung note a tap whistles when filling a vase
showing the business end of flowers.

Alex MacDonald

Keep Apart Two Chevrons

a roadside majesty
two petrol stations
facing each other
one green and
one orange against
a purple sunrise
some are asleep
at slip roads
others are exhausted
in orthopaedic chairs
on their way
to molecular dramatics
with cat eyes
hairpins and hard
shoulders to grip

(

This Unnatural Valley While We Speak So Low

I'm not home right now - country roads go both ways

getting lost becomes contrary motion - a discipline of blurring out

hay bales five storeys high - a building of dead residents

a wall made now broken - I don't own anything here

me and two friends alone - our conversation stirs between us

I'm stunted by the possibilities - I hope it isn't obvious

walking is necessary and boring - what's there to think about

all this becomes sludge eventually - trees fall and birds melt

the future as moody teenager - everything black with flame detail   )

a spider watches me piss - eight eyes can't see shit

this open world those owls - unaware of the road's incline

we decide music beats poetry - bad poetry is about holidays

we unpick these decisions quickly - what's important is your playfulness

how you interpret wild harps - wind through the telegraph wires

Mordents

other thoughts hold me up
if it isn't light on a brick wall
it's the shadow cast by a crane
a mark across the heart
or the surface of a pond
with its own green culture
what hinges do I swing on
which two rooms do I connect
the work floor and the nurse's office
a cellar with a fur coat of dust
and this flight of stairs
so frequently I am between two places
two ideas like the twin walls
of a trash compactor
helpfully reducing all options
to a single premise

(

Leonie Rushforth

–

Object Love

Six no seven white pots of divers sizes,
not so different from each other, one dimpled
with indeterminate shapes and a little smaller,
another bigger, flared, fluted – each

exerts or expresses – what is it? –
not so much a pressure as a purity of longing
for you to need it, love it, become part of it
and you do, you do. Your heart goes out to them.

And I see they will have to go with you
everywhere, even unto the claggy grave.
And here behind the cupboard door
is the too-big scarified brown pot

)

you have never found a use for but
now you hug it to your unmotherly dugs
and weep into it O humble receptacle
for everything that matters and is holy.

Lochlan Bloom

–

The Unquietable Hum

I was nine years old when the man came to take my father away.
I was the one who opened the door, the one who let the man into our
house, so in a sense you could say it was my fault. But that would be
unfair, I was only nine after all, I could not have been expected to know
what was happening or understand what goes through the minds of
grown-ups.

I have rationalized events since then of course, gone over the
details and explicated things, but there still remains a lingering doubt
that my life would have been much different if I had simply ignored the
bell that day.

It was a perfectly ordinary Thursday. I had returned from school an
hour before and had already eaten my snack. Every day when I came
home I would have a glass of milk and, when it was just my mother at
home, a piece of fruit.

(

On that particular Thursday of course my father happened to be at
home and that meant that I was allowed to have a biscuit or even a
small cake, dependant what was in the kitchen. I am still not sure of
the logic behind this but somehow my father's presence in the house
meant greater leniency.

I never remember him explicitly stating that I should have biscuits
instead of fruit or indeed any sort of discussion on the topic. There was
simply the rule that snack time involved biscuits when father was
at home.

He worked a shift pattern as a post office administrator so
most days when I got home from school he wasn't there but roughly
once every two weeks his shifts meant that he worked evening
cover instead.

It was always mum that emerged from the bedroom first, tucking
her dressing gown around her waist, and bending to give me a kiss as
I came in the door.

Hello, Ben, she would say. *Good day at school?*

I didn't speak much at that age so I would normally just nod and
throw my bag in the corner under the stairs. Mum would lead me into

the kitchen, past my parents closed bedroom door, talking all the while about my classes and busying herself asking me questions. Only once I was seated at the kitchen table, eating my biscuits and milk, would my father finally emerge, tugging at his belt, his shirt flapping haphazardly.

Even at the age of nine I had my suspicions about what the two of them might be doing in bed in the middle of the day but I knew that my arrival at three thirty marked the end of their activities. I didn't know exactly what my parents got up to before I arrived but I was sure in the knowledge that when I came in the door they would drop their tedious grown-up tasks and join me.

On this occasion events transpired as usual. My father entered, ruffled my hair and helped himself to a piece of shortbread from the plate in the middle of the table.

Good day, Ben? he said.

He was jaunty, I would almost say cheerful, as if a pressure had lifted off him. He normally had a gentleness about him of the sort that borders on melancholy so it was a surprise to see him so upbeat.

We lived in a meagre house and while we were certainly not poor I was at the start of that age where I realised that we had less material wealth than other families. After that fateful afternoon the point was certainly rammed home with more force but even before then I think I had an inkling that greed, avarice and lust were important building blocks of adult life.

It is hard now to precisely describe the emotions or feelings in those short minutes as we three sat around the table, eating shortbread and slurping milk. My remembrance of that scene has no doubt been altered with the intervening year, based on all that happened afterwards. There are too many conflicting feelings to give a truly accurate picture.

In any case, we can't have been there more than ten minutes. My father left and went back into the bedroom, closing the door behind him, and my mum went upstairs to tidy. We lived in a modest house near the outskirts of town. There was a dining room attached to the kitchen and a separate lounge downstairs. Upstairs my brother and I had separate rooms and there was a second toilet. More than enough space for all of us.

)

My brother was ten years older than me so we seldom fought. I often wonder what it would have been like to have a brother closer to my own age. Would he have bullied me? Or I bullied him? I knew boys at school that were always fighting with their brothers but I envied them the closeness of their relationship.

My brother had grown distant ever since we had moved house. Until I was about four we lived in a smaller place and the two of us shared a room. I'm not sure if it was this closer proximity, or simply the fact that my brother entered puberty, but as soon as we had moved into our new rooms he was like a foreigner to me.

He smoked cigarettes out of his window and sulked about with his headphones on, muttering monosyllables now and again in way of response to questions. I idolised him still but I didn't feel like I had known him for years.

He went to college on the other side of town and never returned before about seven. Often he would stay at friend's houses or not return until after I had gone to bed. In any case I knew he would be leaving soon to go to uni so I had become accustomed to thinking of the family without him.

I had some homework to do so mum set out my books on the kitchen table and left me to get on with it. I was a good student at that age. None of the tasks were particularly taxing and I didn't really consider any alternatives other than doing what I was told.

People that have met me in certain periods of my adult life have been surprised to hear that I was so diligent as a child. Some shake their head and smile as if I am making a joke when I tell them that I never bunked off school once.

It would normally take me around twenty minutes to complete my homework and then I would go upstairs to play, or if the weather was good outside into the street. On that Thursday however the problems our maths teacher had set us were a little trickier and I remember taking longer than usual to complete them.

I was the closest to the door when the bell went and, frustrated at my inability to finish the homework, I rushed at the opportunity of a diversion. As I approached the front door I could see the outline of the man through the frosted glass. The door had a burlap pattern that created a distorted silhouette similar to a reflection in a choppy lake.

When I opened the door I was greeted by a man of about my father's age. He had rough stubbly skin and wore a leather jacket. His skin was dark, tan, like a camel. His clothes were covered in a layer of dust and he had a tired look about him as if he had walked all the way into town and really wanted to sit down. Despite his fatigued look, his eyes twinkled and he smiled at me broadly as I peered around the half open door.

Hello there, he said. *Does Michael live here?*

I didn't know what he meant to begin with. My father's name was Michael but everyone called him Mike. I doubt I had ever heard anyone refer to him as Michael before that point so I merely stood in the doorway looking at him in confused silence.

Is your dad here? he continued undeterred, his eyes shining. It was only then that the penny dropped and I nodded dumbly to the man. Without saying a word I turned back into the house, leaving him on the doorstep, and knocked on my father's door. He appeared instantly, in his shirt.

Mmmmh, he said

Dad, there's a man at the door for you, I said.

Who is it?

I don't know.

My father emerged and squeezed past me, along the corridor to the front door. As soon as he saw who it was I realised that something momentous had happened. My father's whole body stiffened and he gulped in a deep breath of air.

Michael, the man at the door said.

You're here! My father seemed to be having difficulty speaking and leant heavily against the door frame. *Amal, I thought... I didn't think I would...*

I tried to hear more but my father stepped outside onto the porch, practically closing the door behind him. The two of them talked in hushed tones and through the glass I could make out that they hugged.

I didn't know what to make of this development and stood in the hall waiting for my father to come back inside. I was sure it must be someone new from his work. He never normally had friends call round and I was pretty sure I knew his existing work colleagues.

The two of them talked for no more than a couple of minutes before my father poked his head around the door.

Sandra, he shouted, *I'm going out for a bit. I'll be back later.*

I remember his face quite distinctly in that moment, there was a crazed sort of energy in his expression and his eyes looked like two dark suns. Despite the fact that I was no more than a metre and a half from him he looked straight past me. I never saw my father again.

By the time my mother rushed downstairs the front door was closed and the pair of them had gone.

What was that? my mother asked, flustered.

Dad's gone out, I said, relaying the message he had shouted up the stairs.

He didn't say where?

No. The man came to the door then they went off.

I could see that my mother was as confused as I was. It was not normal behaviour for my father to disappear like that.

Who was it? my mother asked, evidently ticking off possibilities in her head.

I don't know, an old man, I said. *I think dad called him Amal?*

Again, I cannot say what effect the intervening years have had on my recall but it seemed to me then that my mother physically shrank when I said this name.

Amal? she repeated, as if in a trance.

She led me back to the kitchen but I could tell that she was preoccupied. She laid out more shortbread and milk and then, when I told her I had already eaten, she tutted to herself and poured the milk down the sink.

I settled back into my seat to finish off the maths homework but she shook her hand at me, absent-mindedly.

Don't worry about that today, dear, she said. *Go upstairs and play.*

I was unsure what to make of this, as it was a cast iron rule that I finished my homework before I could play, but in this instance I thought it best to do as I was told.

Upstairs I busied myself with my Lego bricks working on a wall for the castle I had been building. Through the open door of my bedroom I heard my mother talking to someone on the phone. Her voice sounded emotional and one or two times I thought she might be crying but when I stopped to listen closer I couldn't be sure.

After several hours, I was hungry and since we never ate later than seven o'clock I went downstairs to ask my mother when dinner would be. I found her in the kitchen still on the phone.

We'll wait for your father, she said.

And so we waited. I watched TV and my mother fretted about the lounge, attempting to tidy the place up. It was only when my brother finally arrived home at nine o'clock that we were eventually allowed to eat.

Is dad working tonight? he asked, halfway through the meal.

I looked to my mother to see if she would reveal any more but she simply bit her lip and nodded. My brother didn't seem to notice anything awry but it confused me that my mother should nod, as if in agreement to his question.

After dinner I think I must have finished my homework and then we all watched TV in silence. I didn't say any more about the mysterious man that had arrived at the door but I could tell my mother was still thinking about him.

As she was tucking me in that evening I asked:

Mum, who was that man?

He's a good friend of your father's, Ben, that's all, she replied.

In the first few days that followed my mother was stoical, keeping up her day-to-day routine as if my father had simply nipped out to the shops. I think it was probably a week before I realised that everything had fundamentally changed.

My grandparents came to stay and I remember lots of heated discussions between them and my mother, behind the closed door of the lounge. They told me very little, or anything that they did say meant very little to me as a nine-year-old. It took me years to get the full story.

I carried on as usual but a curiosity started to gnaw at me. It was my grandfather who finally sat me down and told me.

Ben, he said. *Your dad's gone away and he might not be coming back for a very long time.*

I nodded, uncomprehendingly.

You remember that man that came to the door?

Amal? I asked, pleased that I had remembered the unusual name.

31

Yes, Amal, my grandfather said, evidently picking his words carefully. A strange look flickered across his face. *Well he knows your dad. Amal is a friend of your dad's. They grew up together, when your dad lived abroad, you remember?*

Indeed I had heard my father's stories of growing up in the Middle East. His parents had been expats in Oman and he had been born out there. My father would often mention the country fondly, telling me and my brother that we would visit there one day.

He's not a friend of dad, I said angrily. *I know all dad's friends.*

Well not all of them. He hadn't seen Amal for a very long time but he loves him very much.

Mum loves dad very much, I said. I had no doubt heard these sorts of euphemisms before.

Yes she does, my grandfather continued, *but, sometimes, people make stupid decisions when they're in love.*

Has mum made a stupid decision? I asked, confused about what my grandfather was getting at.

No, he said, shaking his head. *No, she hasn't done anything wrong, Ben, don't worry. It's just that, sometimes, being in love with someone can be the hardest thing in the world.*

Well, I am no longer nine years old, I have seen much of life in the intervening years, and though I have travelled East and West, North and South, fathoming untold depths, in all that time my grandfather's words have remained with me, buzzing around my ears like an angry bee.

Sam Buchan-Watts

–

Forum Bar (For Lauri Love)

To leave a digital footprint that's out of step
with Stradishall, Suffolk. Some future
for the son of a former
British Baptist Minister.
To smile wide in the face of
grey rain / atopic eczema
– smile not wiped by
computer / tabloid paper. To have
considered all the evidence and data
to rock the boat so as to touch both
sides of the water – people died for the right
to see the evidence, others kept on constant watch
/ psychotropic medication so as to hold
some semblance of the smiling / guilty person.

)

Computer Fraud and Abuse Act (For Aaron Swartz)

To give back borrowed data
no meaningful return of what's stolen
when everyone gets a copy
'return' as submit, split from 'recall'
retract, undo send / these shadows offended
behind a bike helmet / ACER laptop
to access material produced at public research
institutions / private institutions with public funding
via public WIFI / in a network closet at MIT
the online equivalent of checking
too many books out of library
people are still talking confidently
in terms of online equivalents
the integrity of the printed object
he could be lending them out
could be boyish curiosity / a fine line
between merely imp / and prison camp
buying or borrowing a culture with a poster
for a meticulous planner / bankrupting
everyone you know / barristers chambers
of the heart / breaking and entering
beautiful smiling boy / is it not about
everything you put out into the world
no return / no valency / sorry

(

Dominic Jaeckle & Hoagy Houghton

—

February 3rd

)

When you sent me a translation of a poem by Alberta Pimenta
I felt you knew that things were smoked out.

You were right, of course,
and we are always looking for different categories,
different compressions,
different ways to arrange objects on the table.

Your name carrying all the weight for a little time.

> *Have you noticed that you have*
> *The entire world*
> *Inside your head*
> *And that world in a brutal*
> *Compression*

February is always piecemeal. I clock a note in my notebook about oat-
meal from the previous week and try to write a piece about breakfast in
America. I think I have eaten breakfast in America around two hundred
or so times over the course of my life, which feels enough, by memory,
to begin thinking on a law of averages. But, to focus so on the morning,
the rest of the day ends up all swamped in vaults of fog.

> *& have you noticed that I have*
> *The entire world*
> *Inside my head*

I imagine you moving, and I think about the resonance and weight of
the title 'A Command of Silence'.

> *And that world*
> *In a brutal compression*
> *Is my world*
> *Which right now is not going into*
> *You*
> *Not through your eyes*
> *But through the names*

(

For what you have inside your head
and what I have inside my head
being the names of the world in a brutal
compression

I still keep a napkin on my desk I was given on a domestic flight between two towns in my early twenties. The napkin carried the name of Coca-Cola in twelve languages. The airport is always an emotional site. A suite for conjugation. The domestic terminal was divided into two distinct areas – that much was not unusual – crossing the line from one side to the other was an act of submission – endemic of a will to be moved. Delta was the only operational airline for the south terminal, and a delta was an image propitious enough to outline some sort of touching declaration. We imagine the source, the slow, early work of the river that self-defines as *river*. It's naming itself after itself as it carves out the borders of its banks. It gets wider and wider. It gets harder to cross. Its mouth is then open so wide that the two lips that cap its borders become difficult to distinguish from the land that grounds its edges. The river doesn't exist anymore. It's a flat delta. The delta gets quieter as it widens. Now we have to talk about the ocean.

)

in a way, it's not you who knows the
world
nor me who knows the world
but it's the names that you know that
know the world
and it's the names that I know that
know the world

A collection of works on the difference between Coca-Cola, Royal Crown and Pepsi; a portmanteau of scenes called *Mountain Dew*; thinking about a body of work as a body of water.

which enters into you and which enters into me
through the names it already has
in a way that what enters through my

37

eyes cannot
enter through your eyes
but only through your head through
the names given by my head
to what came into my eyes already
with names
and in the same way
what enters through your eyes cannot
enter through my eyes
but only through my head through
the names given by your head
to what enters through your eyes already with
names

I dream about cloudbanks and the hidden peaks of mountains. Seen from either above or below. The significance of which is tiresome. A piece of satire in some Internet daily charts a picture of the 'thirty most disappointing under thirty'. In that pool, there is a remark on an archetype, aged twenty-nine, who started writing a screenplay. She tells at least thirty friends and family members about the project and never finishes it. I wake up wondering whether the mountain was the person or the product.

and so what you see
is already inside you before
you see it
and so, what I see
is already inside me before
I see it
and everything you might see up close,
or beyond the names,
is unspeakable and stays inside you
and all I might see is closer
or beyond their names
is unspeakable and stays inside me
and it is like this that we go on building
ourselves for the second time
you to yourself, me to myself...

building an unrepeatable and non-transferable
consciousness
more and more intense in itself.

You in yourself
me in mine

)

Cathleen Allyn Conway

—

At Least I'm Pretty

Her eyebrows mock me in the mirror.   She sways;
                                       limbs so smooth, so willowy-tall.
                                       Brackish liquid dribbles
down her legs. Her luminous lips move.
I can't find my face in that silver veil.

Maybe   a vampire takes over someone else
                                       not to see their reflection in a mirror,
                                     but in another person's face. Her face

ethereal, her feathery voice a seasick wall of sound.
The faces of virgins aren't even pretty.

I'll never be like this,   hair rising in jeopardy flames, a pearl-fluid
                                     breeze in a clock-cry of stillness, a
                                     demon of doom tilting on a trapeze.

My brain will never work right.
I need to study the dark until it takes shape.

(

18 and Still Human

Look at her. Who is she; it doesn't say?
She's pretty coiffed:

unraveled red roses singing in her hair, drinking her coffee like original sin, wounding with a flourish of her fatal whip.

It'll hurt like hell.

In Bluebeard's study he makes love to her cold dissected body on a narrow cot, doing it every night whether her heart wants it or not, every time like the first time.

Imagine:

enter her realm, become part of it, the light and shrieks and mysterious symbols and language left by clarion birdmarks in sand, phantoms that swim from the recesses of memory,   )

thin little girls with shadowed eyes and bloody thighs.

Imagine: 18 and still

Hisham Bustani
trans. Maia Tabet

–

Orchestra

[First Movement]

She was seated at the black piano. The music had evaporated from her head, and only crooked melodies stumbled from her fingers. When she turned around, his eyes were looking straight into hers, and the kiss he blew into the air teased her lips. When she placed her slender fingers inside his mouth, the crookedness of the melodies receded; and when their two bodies joined, the place reverberated with music.

[Second Movement]

In the hall, there was complete silence—other than for the speaker's stammering voice; and for the early protestations of a baby, whose victorious utterances propelled his mother outside; and for the ringing of the cell phone in the back, when the audience learned of the beloved's name and that 'Encounter between Byzantine and Arab Civilizations: Samples of their Poetry' was simply the cover for the lovers' planned tryst.

It was her turn now. He stopped noticing the heavy breathing of the couple behind him; the brassy woman's explosive clapping at her daughter's first recitation of poetry in public (never mind that she didn't understand it, what really mattered was the extra grade in class); the feigned interest of the security detachment; and even the glaring look of the Almighty Leader staring menacingly from the frame hanging in the middle of the hall.

It was her turn: the cadence slid into place, and the words flowed in lilac streams across the podium and between the seats. Now alone, he bathed in the fields of his childhood, scaling the clouds of his longing and scattering like flower petals on the warm breeze.

She carried him far away, to the distant place where tears swelled into torrents.

When he left hurriedly to go to his car, her smiling gaze bid him good-bye, blue had cleaved from blue, and colour saturated everything: the speaker, the Almighty Leader's portrait, the security men, and all

(

42

of the phonies in the hall. With him, in the back seat of the car, was the couple that had sat behind him in the hall, while she slipped into the passenger seat to scatter her colours along the pavement.

[Third Movement]

Afterwards, she'd sat in his lap while they read what they could in the way of poetic verses, wrapping their bodies around the music of the words:

The ballerina, who had tumbled from her lips only moments earlier, leapt into the air and snaked across the winding river of fire on the floor. Naked, she circled the perimeter of the body swollen with desire, ascending towards her writer who sat god-like and aloof upon the sofa (or so she thought) where he counted each breath and gathered falling stars, fortune-tellers' signs, and what to the listening ear are ciphers of inspiration, packing them all into the jumble of his brain to conjure them up with ink on the desert of parched white paper.

But her writer—the one who is contaminated by minds outside his own, and chafes against bodies made of flesh, igniting the brazier's spark that lights the coal-stack propelling the driving wheels which overturn the rusty engine of time ... That writer of hers was not the One, the Unparalleled, the Everlasting. He was hewing his way through a forest of desire, erupting from pomegranate breasts, gulping down the liquor of saliva, and biting on the stretch of alabaster that led to the promontory of bliss and down to the delta of pleasure. That writer of hers generated fire, piercing the Mother's grass with the Father's flint until their creamy froth mixed.

The ballerina was furious. She raged and she screamed, then realised that her feet rested on the cadence of the two bodies, that her dance was born of their climax, that the melodies she held aloft rose and fell to the rhythm of the gasps cascading from her lips and his.

The ballerina understood that her resurgence dwelled in the fevered delirium of the two joined bodies.

* * *

The night lit up by love was over. The ballerina folded herself back into the white pages and lay down to sleep between the words. She would rise again—the fortune-tellers had told her so—but only when poetry became soft fingertips prying open shirt-buttons.

43

Iain Britton

–

The Strawberryalarmclock

tilts its thin-stretched hands
the jug boils

& the worm sambas
by lamplight, the worm syphons the air
zooms in on the heatwave of a town

the jug boils & time leans sharply
on its axis. the earth's voice

slips out its tongue. the earth
speaks of wetlands & green hair
knotted in mud

(the strawberryalarmclock lip-reads
thoughts, tracks movements up streets
past boys & girls. their high-jinx clatter

the wooden lookalikes of this house
fit names to names
& the descending axis of time leans sharply

under this roof, carved divinities
follow my actions

i touch the features
of my father & mother their son
a community holding hands &
never letting go. how delicate

is narcissism
how dangerously delicate to live within
the dimensions of a red-stained pool

of brittle flowers

the strawberryalarmclock

leans sharply on its axis. the jug boils
& i imagine someone shuffling courtesies

i drink a cubist's perception of a cloud

floating in coffee.

)

Black Polarities

small things matter. a church

stirs fiery flecks from punctured hands. red sunlight
slides across the floor

i swoop in, scan for cracks, for clearances & then swoop out

past 4th world geographies
past hills & gorges
freshwater lakes, forests made for flightless birds

but you, you have become an invisible formless guest
spinning between the black polarities of the universe

where there's no indication of gravity's grip, no programme for re-entry
to a life surrounded by fucked-up angels

(

you're nothing but a hot shifting emotion, that's all

with you, i hang on to this giant green finger, this belief
for one day more.

Jazmine Linklater

—

Atargatis: Her Salt

I.

The gallery floor carries her lying in pieces; bones' eyes peer at your looking in ceramic & steel. She's all offcuts. Residues. Parts. She almost always isn't but glitters still surface electrical clichés despite her plucked smooth down ground feathers to powder & dried sea-foam bottled, compressed tight making lightless. Rolled horizons in multiple melting mist into solid & preserved in smoked air: denying all possibility still inside her of liquid.

II.

She was wanted stacked, tight sheath-dressed column right out arms angled. Like the altar floats, moves in the water. But camouflage disobeyal concrete again: we lie down in protest in pieces in the undergrowth, kitchen, desert and forest. We're eating; we're looking. Doves & fish. Price lists & storage solutions. It rains: her flanks rise)
& fall with the atmosphere's weight. Residual music sings the kuliltu in moisture: sword in, right up to the hilt.

Victory (two ways)

I.

See how here at the edge of the object
it isn't the end but the seam where you join
face on, lips pursing a kiss's round O
& blowing hot torrents of air so lung's gale
cascades your sea-salt (from tongue,
cheeks, roof)—it flies, dances, flecks
the prow, the hip points, thigh & breast
pressing her garments against her
(chiton, tunic) & damp billows show
Sappho's thin fire racing below skin,
violets stream out behind her
from fabric's dark folds (cloak, himation)
sews sails & your wind layers feathers
(not as nature or art) & her thunder moves up
to meet yours (she's not trembling).

(

II.

Some objects are objects & other, their edges
ends (walls without openings). The seam
here's not fluid. Sing salt spray she starts
to dissolve, moulded garments temporarily glued
(as paper, as tape). You're working on memory,
can't stir this. She's hung & you're punctured,
deflating. What's growing swells elsewhere
& lives (but not here) – this strength's origami:
a trick, a sigh, admission. (To be how
what you both.) She's undressed
& scarpered (cloak, himation discarded,
bunched) & you are left longing.
Thin fire that raced under skin
only smoulders, your waiting layering
ineffectual wings: silent (you're trembling).

Inanna: Her Face

I.

Her eye's ear's turned above, set from and turned below. Soft to wedded stillness concretes children's absent hands: she's given, she'll gather back all dawn has sundered: whorl kisses speech marks, shells, chants beneath her gaze utterance engulfs: lapis lazuli sky sky pomegranate neons, chanting moss breathes breathing moss; oil sweets violets sweets cedar coalesce her colours: she becomes she becomes she gathers child's making unto others, would usher mother where a child might draw: technician might make might knowing may skill but otherwhere. She gathers deep sound, shroud, dressed offcuts dressed purple in folds.

II.

But sweet mother loom's bust, corners snagged sentences spilt sickly clovers slick juniper sticky: pushed my face into a blossoming kisses, mouth filled mulch value tasting emulsion and think: playing, not catching and carrying, co-opted sky star-jammed in packaging: sacharined apricots, jellies dated dissolve but meat rots exquisite when hook-hung on walls, exquisite, imagine—giving and giving, baby's breath scattered all round as a filler; painted all white some starting over again, some rebirth's aborted libation: wine, vodka, soap; joss sticks import burns, opens faux holiday window.

)

Meryl Pugh

–

from *Wife of Osiris*

A field of flowered and seeding grasses, waist-high.

She is wearing red, he is wearing his gold aspect.

The seeds ascend, corona of light around each hard particle.
Ascend. Then it's

the ground disappearing and day flicking to night each colour
to its opposite each object to its other side each being to its
other face but
        still, the ascending:

(

flecks of radiant everything coming loose and warm.

His gift today: flight. She swoops above the city's river like a swallow – like, in fact, the birds around her: not swallows, small, long tails, navy tufts either side of the head, the whole flock landing, now, on the water.

Then, dark, underneath, racing her shadow: a school of many large fish. One rises towards a little bird, opens its mouth. Good for the fish, she thinks, accepting the bird's death – but the bird twitches away. Good for the bird.

Her shadow picks up speed on the choppy grey shine as the school curves away. Then, white spray, leaping: submarine, orca, goddess rising? Grey porpoises break surface – two columns proceeding in stately manner upstream.

Who has called such creatures? Who schools these wild things to such a showing? Not Osiris, absented again. For she has lost his gift, is coughing and paddling in their wake.

)

Elizabeth Reeder & Amanda Thomson
–
microburst

(

what you do not remember somehow resides here in this room where you've been taken, your swollen legs are red-angry like a sky in storm at dusk with silver-coated bandages over their weeping and **you can feel but can't see the broken horizon-lines that puncture the peaceful coast of your neck** and folds of skin hang down and then retreat with the thanksgiving days and with the meds they give you, and your hands are skinny for all that, veins popping over the bones, over the knobs of arthritis or gout (they don't know which), and in sleep you raise your head on the inhale as if to make room in your busy chest for air and your chin falls down when you're empty and the floor is where you were found a few days ago, taken by a fast shock which sent you not to your knees but flat onto your back, your heart so slow, face so swollen that **for more than a few seconds she thought you were dead** and through the yellow of your eyes you do not always recognize us and mom has to sign the form, we have to trust you'll not die here on the table, and trust that you might die if we don't sign, and the level of doctor-nurse activity says it all, this could be it, **this is it**   and   after   three days in ICU they you move to CCC and the shirt you wear over your gown gives you just enough decency to barter with a realtor over the details of the weirdly demanding offer of someone wanting to buy the house you've lived in for thirty-two years and it's home to some, a reluctant sale if it goes through, but stairs are stairs (you want mom to be safe too) and your legs are your legs and now your burning feet aren't even eager to take you someplace slowly and **you're not afraid of the point of departure but traveling there is nothing but painful**, recalling how you're losing your forty acres   all the blinds up in the house when you and mom usually keep them down and in this autumn night **when I look up, my brother beside me, the house ablaze with lights, your den looks Rockwell-esque, like poetry**, and the number crunching business of heading a family takes on **the timbre and rhythm of elegy, a dirge**   the light, the warm light hitting off the wood of your office shelves, the organizational logic of which you always protested you had despite the splayed piles of papers, the piles on piles, the very breath of to-do the room held and you exhaled and the papers flew into place via my hands but it was faster than I'd imagined and you didn't diminish with it despite a fiction-prediction but **I'm not sure the move won't kill you or that mom's reaction to the move won't kill us both   she worries,** repeats phrases, the action like rubbing oose between fingers or sunburned skin peeled and worried between fingertips and sand in an oyster pearl pearl please let it be a pearl and the irritation will be worth it, for the words she says, the same words the same words same order a loop a loop she's knitting knitting her face like a dropped stitch and loop loop, **I don't want to sell my house, I don't want to sell**, I don't want to sell and it is a forced move but it's not me or dad or anyone

)

but this life which doesn't play by the rules or respect the timetables you have in your head and **you've had your share of injustices and they loop, loop in your head, out your lips** and it's tiring to listen to back in August the streets are flooded, the power is out, and the wind explodes drops of rain into horizontal needles which pierce trees which give up their limbs and **it's just a moment of extreme force within an ongoing storm** it's an albatross, I yell during the microburst, no electricity, no lights, and the door hits dad's leg and here's the sudden jolt back into illness butted against death as the EMTs come and track rainwater and storm-mud through your house, borrowing a flashlight because the lights are out and they carry him out to the ambulance and we're imprisoned in the dark house together and it's crowded with your worry **this house is a fucking albatross**, I repeat and you get angry and it's a Parkinson's anger, different, I can't explain it but I know it, know that it's altered, exaggerated from what has always been here and **you're a top that's been spinning just fine for years and then it slows wobble wobble wobble** and I'm watching and you still feel the spinning and it has always worked before and why not now, why not now, my logic has always worked before, and why not now and why and why not the breaks between the words aren't steady aren't empty they're filled with the gears of your brain getting stuck, jerking forward I've always been able why not now because all has changed and anyone can see it, **strangers see it, how we're all in crisis**, how it's a mess, and they see us emergency off-kilter, at risk the storm is steady with sure gusts as if his falls don't say it clearly enough: the first one in February, the broken foot, and then the one in April he hid that I'm still not supposed to know about which now seems minor, and the next one in May, a break as well, a wrist, and then the next one out of bed in a storm in the August heat and bruised ribs (and maybe the hip, opening up the landscape to November's hemotoma) and the next in November which led him to be lying for hours on the cold floor with infection speed of light speed of poisoned blood through him, through his heart unable even on a good day to do its job, and the cold and the bugs in his blood made it thick and the cheering section was asleep and his heart has its own tenacity and kept on beating, his body heating up his legs so angry, so angry, and his eyes yellow with mucus and sometimes he didn't know who I was, who he was, and it's the worst I've seen him people see him as a frail old man and so in the ER when he says he feels worse than when he came in I tell the doc, the young capable doctor, **that dad never complains and they need to pay attention because he never complains**, he never even tells us things we need to know, although he's getting a bit better and yet the whole thing is getting more subtle as if running away from his decisions not to face it and it's running and he can't give chase, he can't on some

(

days even give a glance and we're playing a game on ice and we're trying to rub the ice before him to make the surface smooth, fast enough or slow enough to hit its mark   **we're frantic and deep down this leads to a leaden slowness and when I'm staring into space near the end of the first week of his hospitalization in November my mom says that my stare is just like Parkinson's and she laughs and I don't know her at all** and in her head it must be a wild landscape uniquely hers and confusing and I'm pretty sure a compass wouldn't work in there because she could convince herself of almost any change of direction or definition, if it suited her, and she's moving better but is exhausted with real reason of course and it's too much for all of us and even at a distance **my brother and sister are all torn up, and my mom says we'll all be devastated when dad dies and she's right**

.

.

.

three days away isn't long or enough and the first night back I'm desperate for a drink, to lose just a minute, to lose myself for just a minute and I gulp down the red wine you bought, a thick Bordeaux, cold like winter and warming too, it's this bottle we drink out of tall glasses because we can't be bothered to handwash the wine goblets   I knock it back like you see them glug whisky in the movies and it hits me all at once after dinner at the end of a day when my mom could only be described as completely batty, affected, exhausted, and no wonder and there's all these reasons but that doesn't change the fact that I'm at the end of my tether necessarily, a desired half-cut and me **wanting to stop   stop**   to not have to handle her, not have to talk smoothly and calmly and always reasoning when reason has left her, especially today when she's crazy, loopy, and off subject or always back on that same subject back and back she's the curl of hair you twist and twist till it pops out, find it again, twist twist and each time it's too much even when we know more, even when more is familiar, it's too much and when **she doesn't let up on her loop, when she tells me I've not been there enough I crack**, and then my brother is here and hasn't yet found a way to talk to her and he snaps too, and is working as hard as he can and it's a one-way street because she can't see his efforts or that she has to work too, on many of the same issues, and so it's hitting his head against a brick wall or sticking his fingers through the weak weave of her knitting loop loop worry worry and you can't quite tune her out, it's the pitch of the thing, the ring of truth but it's distorted and you can't ignore it, **white noise, every white noise has its own pitch you can test it,** someone has, and she's the droning of a ceiling fan, the struggled clicking of the heat when it can't quite turn itself on

)

(from *MICROBURSTS*)

Sinae Park

—

Swimmers

(

)

(

)

Michael Egan

—

small beauties

now time gets to the core   for sorrow, the magpie sang and the boy scavenged for batteries in river mud   they're called mudmen these people but I don't think they were born from mud, I think it's just their lives are baked clay hard, unmalleable, waiting to be dropped and shatter   that song, on strings, is fearsome, it carries a weight of importance language can't get at   listen, sometimes fires are set to give life a chance to grow   and ash is merely song, listen   so seasons speed on, increased or encouraged   slipping away into another decade   soon there'll be some other hatred   some other split   some other politics I have no faith in   there they are, the solid men the molded men   she images them, not imagines   she writes little phrases like *rain flesh* and *dusk cold*   now speeding up, we are jumping forward, our lives buffering   so I crave not love, not broken honour, not betrayal   when we sleep those men are moving along the river, searching   a siren wakes them, she sings for them   we hear it and think of war   how close we must be now to some ending, some fracturing   they are shapes upon shapes skulking along the river all the way to the estuary   below the bridge they wash each other of the night's grime   in our bathroom we wash each other of whatever tainted us   small beauties, I can't find them   small beauties, they're gone   soft longing, it echoes and shifts again as if over-sung siren, it wails for them   gold flakes or gazeth not   he wears bright shoes call someone you never knew, let them steal his eyes and there's creation there, in that theft of images   you need to write all this down, distort it, Michael   make mud of it   make it a struggle for others to form images from, to hammer at and make true when there is not a shred of that   let them break it all so you can't be blamed   innocence   or pleasure arrives late, apologizes for the traffic and compliments us on the colour scheme, on the Moroccan tiles we never bought, on the way we fit together as if we were sculpted, moulded as one   go deep into the quarry, dig out every ounce of mud   try aching love, distort us.

(

only replication at the river

I said we should make a replica of this day because I'm not afraid to follow
my instincts   it was a week before school started   it was twenty three
years ago   in spite of everything they looked good together, every last
one of them, like heads in baskets staring up at a guillotine's blade   and
then all of a sudden there were horses descending into the river, one girl
clinging to a mane then letting go and drowning in laughter as her sister
screamed for the mare to keep going   a man on the riverbank screaming
for the water to lower, to reveal those who had already been lost   and at
the edge of it all was a woman who had drowned unnoticed   I waved to her
but she didn't wave back   and then all of a sudden I saw someone else fall
into the water   a second figure leap from the bridge   once they leapt
like this every summer, now they only leap when there's a need   like death
not to save the drowned, you have to understand that   if you understand
one thing, understand that   they are leaping because they don't believe
drowning is possible   they don't believe anyone ever has drowned despite
the bodies floating face down, despite their own losses   there is an email
doing the rounds about a General Election   I bring that in here because   )
change is drowning, because politics is drowning, because democracy is a
form of drowning these days   I can't ask these people political questions,
they're too much like me   we haven't voted since 1997   and anyway they're
too busy swimming   I can't see myself ever standing for parliament, I
can't see myself surviving in a river like this with so many bodies competing
for space   I can't see the boy rising from the water, perhaps he too is a
drowned child   all the kids were watching him with their mouths open
and sunlight pouring out   it's early summer, it's tomorrow afternoon, it's
yesterday and none of this will ever happen because the rain won't stop,
the river will flood and not even the dead woman or the dead boy will be
foolish enough to swim   instead when all of them, every hundred, line
up along the riverbank, drinking, they will take photographs of what might
have been lost.

Molly Ellen Pearson

–

pond skater

i walk into the water

i walk into the water to do so & no other reason

how can i know my reasons

i walk into the water knowing that reason exists only as a word

i walk into the water

the water underneath is yellow yellow & red

it bends forwards

(

how can i know i am walking

that i am not sailing falling an alternate process

that the water is not walking into me

who am i to know

i am walking into the water

how can i tell it is water

how can i feel the difference between myself & it

beneath my deposit of skin there is water

two bodies of water held apart by skin

each with its own face thin & blue as january

perhaps it is not water perhaps

we am together strange fresh thing

i walk into the water

i walked into the water

& it recedes

before me hiding its own extent

how can i know what is down there

how can i know

the hole the water comes from rapt in the lid of my eye   )

how can i tell the water what it knows

!7

the water is caught up in its own question of its own

displaced image bending forwards into the

water i walk

into

i

Olivia Douglass
—
Body Whispers / Acts of Submission

We nearly made it out alive,

Says my body, as it feels me drifting back into the Constant State.

Bruised, desperate, wanting and wanting.

Parts of me have morphed into something to be sold, again.

WHAT HAS HAPPENED:
In the Constant State, individuals bend to the shape of the places they inhabit. Skin stretches across tarmac,
concrete blood, pillars of flesh, here the walls sweat.
Life in the Constant State is a series of Anothers. Another passing Another temperature Another moment Another
exchange Another telling Another look Another trauma. Another one.

A spine snaps, Another crack in the pavement.

Recently, the Constant State has recognized a new form of malfunction. Individuals reacting strongly to cracks.
Each time a spine snaps individuals become prone to body whispers and acts of submission. A crack appears and
the individual suffers devastating levels of soft.
Falls into total collapse and is no longer responsive.

And in this moment,
the individual is temporarily gone, out, not confirmed.

(

We nearly made it out alive,

Says my body, as if to say, you were back for a while, before you slipped away.

And I ask for it to not disturb me, I am here
Breath ing
Cry ing
Sell ing
Bleed ing
Sex ing
Stay ing
Alive.

We nearly made it out alive,

When a crack appears the individual falls into total collapse.

In this moment, it is unconfirmed where they have gone. Once returned, they have never completely arrived, instead functioning in continual suspension between the Constant State and The Gone. When asked where, or what, or how they might be elsewhere individuals have been known to drip from the mouth.

Each drop, if looked at closely enough, contains small images within it.

Of Other passings Other temperatures Other exchange Other tellings Other looks Other life.

Individuals begin to drip from the mouth, such dripping can be identified as foreign language, a form of poetry, a side effect of error.

We nearly made it out alive,

It is becoming harder to ignore these whispers.

We nearly made,

Each invitation to leave, stronger than the one before.

Nearly made it out,

I am becoming devastating levels of soft.

)

We nearly made it out alive,

Says my body, as if to say, come. This time, stay.

And so this time I listen
and I go
swallow the Constant State
gather up my skin, to leave.

Rupert Loydell & Maria Stadnicka
–

THE RUIN OF HERE

'the future is a monotonous instrument'
     – Frances Picabia, 'Blind Man's Bluff'

But we still want to get there,
try to climb the stairs too early,
reach the lighted birds, escape
the ruined castles of our lives.

It looks as though they are flying
but it is only projected shadows
on the bare stone walls. It seems
there is a way out but there isn't:

these earth steps will crumble,
(turn the power off and the light
will fade. We are not suited
to the dereliction of today.

Visiting Hours

I
they no longer
drink tea, listen, squeeze swearwords

at the top floor, a paper-girl tries on black dresses
her teeth bite the blue,
scream; window left open...

life rolls over naked avenues
with a visiting ticket

the nurse comes closer
I collar her, state I am
not through yet

II
they covered orange:)
broken, candle holder,
climbed ladders,
loose living-room socks
hanging
warm neck...
tic-tac! tic-tac!

III
they whisper and nibble and cough
trapped without oxygen masks

silence crumbles,
cars move in the same direction,
well dressed;
my funeral goes ahead

LIVE FOR TODAY

I am trying to read about death
and our attitudes to it; to listen
to the radio discussing a musician
whose name I haven't heard yet.
It's impossible to juggle and balance
any more: life is too complicated
and I enjoy too much. Music, books,
art and film – I want to see and listen
to them all. The music on my radio
repeats and changes, changes
and repeats, chimes into Sunday.

It's Monday and the pianist plays on.
I don't want to move, don't want to
live here, need to go right away;
any day is as good as any other day
for dreaming and planning my escape.
Life's too short and we trap ourselves
with money, houses, things. I have
little to my name, am caught in
revision and reworking of the same.
Today is shot to pieces and time
is running backwards, standing still.

(

Punctus Contra Punctum

From time to time,
we stand between
a wolf and a dog. We germinate
inside tightly zipped handbags
falling into a moment of muteness.

We are expected to root
given the choice of death.

A step closer, a level higher
in a battery operated game:

nobody comes in
without prior agreement.

The recoiled bows springs out
unleashed by a howl.   )

At a steady pace
we catch a moving train.

Anne Vegter
trans. Astrid Alben
–

Late shift

You can sketch out a plan, furnish a new house
but in the half light your foot slips under the floorboards
and you call the corridor a door, door corridor.

You can abandon your search for a light switch:
if your skin withstands the night, sleep yourself awake
on the feathered back of a curious animal.

You can claim this is the try-out but
you measure minutes of light as actually too slow, come
stretch your lips, sweetheart, into a spectacular fermata:

arrive at the galactic platform behind which
(spans a night-net. As the last train pulls out
echoes of stars detonate.

(or would you rather say very last star)
(or reductions)
(or explosions)

You say fabulous sweetheart, how you can hear
your ears slot like keys into the locks
of your startled house.

Late dienst

Je kunt een plan tekenen, een nieuw huis
inrichten maar in halflicht schiet je voet weg
onder de vloer en je noemt gang deur, deur gang.

Je kunt zoeken naar een lichtknop staken:
weerstaat je huid de nacht slaap je wakker
op de veren rug van een nieuwsgierig dier.

Je kunt zeggen dit is de try-out maar
je meet minuten licht als werkelijk te traag toe
rek je lippen, liefste, tot een waanzinnige fermate:

bereik het galactisch perron waarachter
een nachtnet spant, na de laatste trein   )
knallende echo's van sterren.

(of zeg je liever allerlaatste ster)
(of verminderingen)
(of explosies)

Je zegt fabelachtig liefste hoe jij je oren
als sleutels in de gaten hoort vallen
van je geschrokken huis.

(from *Eiland berg gletsjer* [Querido, 2011])   71

Checkpoint

my father said I shouldn't stand out while I was still growing and I ate without weight
his father said the man that betrays his country flogs forgiveness for ovens
his mother said he who know his patrons can marry without god
my mother said the man who betrays his wife will want to birth a murderer
her mother said little red riding hood visited grandmother to kiss her wolf
her father said she shouldn't be afraid actions come before motives
my father said it's not an angel that breaks up parties but dead animals

I said the world's portrayal was adjusted too late because of old decrees
I said the prophecy that became me lies like salt beaten on my scalp
I said in my dreams I escaped this and was loved by detainees
I said I followed the tracks running alongside my dreams, was grabbed that is correct
I said I met no one after such an accident, nothing that weighs more than nothing twice

Checkpoint

mijn vader zei dat ik niet moest opvallen tijdens het groeien en ik at zonder gewicht

zijn vader zei dat de man die zijn land verraadt vergeving verkoopt voor ovens

zijn moeder zei wie zijn opdrachtgevers kent kan een huwelijk sluiten zonder god

mijn moeder zei dat de man die zijn vrouw verraadt een moordenaar wil baren

haar moeder zei dat de roodkapje naar grootmoeder ging om haar wolf te kussen

haar vader zei dat ze niet bang moest zijn daden gaan boven motieven

mijn vader zei niet om een engel worden partijen gestaakt maar om de dode dieren

ik zei dat de voorstelling van de wereld te laat is aangepast dankzij oud gericht

ik zei dat de voorspelling die mij werd als zout geslagen op mijn hoofd ligt

ik zei dat ik in mijn dromen ontsnapte aan deze en geliefd was bij gevangenen

ik zei dat ik naast mijn dromen over rails liep, gegrepen werd je leest het goed

ik zei dat ik niemand aantrof na zo'n ongeluk, niets dat meer weegt dan tweemaal niets

(from *Eiland berg gletsjer* [Querido, 2011])

)

73

Lucy Mercer

–

NOTATION AS MEMORY: THE FIELD OF SYMBOLS

Semibreve rest

Night comes to the countryside. To the water-filled slashes of mud,
the unconventional bramble-brushes, the ivied hawthorns caught
in the hedges breathing out and leaning out into the air like smokers,
hidden and furious. She comes so we might know something of her
daughter the day, who is so silent while performing her activity.
Now all things are melting into each other's arms. No sight but
dark leaves' sight, stretching net, raindrop full invisible and still.
This is why a rest in music is a dark dash — before the clear melody
comes back, as she always does, like the dreaded crunching of
a car lighting its way down a gravel drive at its regular time;
like wanting;

(

(they cross over at the great threshold of the impenetrable bar;
sometimes they do not cross for a long time; when they do not cross
again, the music has stopped).

*

Stave

What an image of images my last hair is? Like an empty field of
long grass on a winter's morning silvered by hundreds of tiny ice
droplets mirroring and mirroring. It is the tide come in across the
hospice pillow, like a woodcut picture of a sea where the mercury
crests are caught falling, though of course they never can be. I have
seen this hair before, in a dream, and I know the startling feeling
of my trainers getting soaked with its coldness. If you look very,
very closely at a patch of it rolling and knotted in itself, you will see
five regular lines which are just five leaves of grass winding in one
continuous strand; the winding face of a staff, which is a caduceus,
held by a messenger wearing nothing but a primrose baseball cap

to keep off the sun. As he walks his footsteps are turned in sheets by the earth's deep orchestra playing a work of love, a quick movement of forgetting.

*

Bass Clef

My childhood pillowcase with cartoon stars and clouds drying on the back of a chair? And the light shining through the cotton like the ladder in a Piero della Francesca painting leading to a closed curtain, always in a closed theatre? That cannot be opened or passed? And the whole indefinable quality of thinking that comes from feeling? How sentimentality plumps the nose? Capillaries inflamed like when grassy seed dust in a gold field raised my back in red lashes? And replica sheep all over the hills with their bells? The metal stamens clanking like tongues? In the language of the heart in distress that time can never be taken back, returned?
As simple as that?   )

Caroline Bergvall

—

thngs dspr

THNGS DSPR THNGS DSPR THNGS DSPR
THNGS DSPR THNGS DSPR THNGS DSPR
THNGS DSPR THNGS DSPR THNGS DSPR
THNGS DSPR THNGS DSPR THNGS DSPR
THNGS DSPR THNGS DSPR THNGS DSPR
THNGS DSPR THNGS DSPR THNGS DSPR
THNGS DSPR THNGS DSPR THNGS DSPR
THNGS DSPR THNGS DSPR THNGS DSPRR
THNGS DSPR THNGS DSPR THNGS DSPR

(

THNGS DSPR THNGS DSPR THNGS DSPR
THNGS DSPR THNGS DSPR THNGS DSPR
THNGS DSPR THNGS DSPR THNGS DSPR
THNGS DSPR THNGS DSPR THNGS DSPR
THNGS DSPR THNGS DSPR THNGS DSPR
THNGS DSPR THNGS DSPR THNGS DSPR
TNNGS THNGS THNGS DSPR THNGS DSPR
THNGS DSPR THNGS DSPR THNGS DSPR
THNGS DSPR THNGS DSPR THNGS DSPR

```
DSPR   DSPR   DSPR   DSPR   DSPR   DSPR
DSPR   DSPR   DSPR   DSPR   DSPR   DSPR
DSPR   DSPR   DSPR   DSPR   DSPR  DDSPR
DSPR   DSPR   DSPR   DSPR   DSPR   DSPR
DSPR   DSPR   DSPR   DSPR   DSPR   DSPR
DSPE  DSPR   DSPR   DSPR   DSPR   DSPR
DSPR   DSPR   DSPR   DSPR   DSPR   DSPR
DSPR   DSPR   DSPR   DSPR   DSPR   DSPR
DSPR   DSPR   DSPR   DSPR   DSPR   DSPR
DSPR   DSPR   DSPR   DSPR   DSPR   DSPR
DSPR   DSPR   DSPR   DSPR   DSPR   DSPR
DSPR   DSPR   DSPR DSPR    DSPR   DSPR
DSPR   DSPR   DSPR DSPR   DSPR    DSPR
DSPR   DSPR   DSPR DSBRR DSBRR   DSPR
DSPR   DSPR   DSPR   DSPR   DSPR   DSPR
DSPR   DSPR   DSPR   DSPR   DSPR DSPR
DSPR   DSPR   DSPR   DSPR   DSPR   DSPR
DSPR   DSPR   DSPI   DSPR   DSPR   DSPR
```

)

Things disappear each side of the waiting. Forms in formations are formed by passing. Through things that pass from one form to the next. They press into forms that relieve from forms. That are stuck in a mould hemmed in by the past. Shapes the unformed with fear.

Or press into crowds that dare to dissolve. To form forms that will shift the ground. And free new shapes from the ground up. Crossing the line between outer forms changes the heart of the mind. Transforms everything from the inside out.

(There's the plant's tendency to seek the light. We no longer cling to our unripening love. It hardened the heart. Made a ghostly pair, a hungry form. Attached, yet divided. Unfree to love, not free to grow.

Lives disappear crushed against the times. I see the uncrossable line. The brutal unchanging powerline that eats at the perpetual hands. That cling and call, then cling and fall and make a long line of corpses. Make a crowd of lined corpses. Crowd of corpses, lines of corpses. Army barracks industrial hangars stadiums full of drowned corpses.

Things disappear like shapes under white sheets. Long shapes and short shapes lined up under stained white sheets. Stretched over shapes that disappear like things under violent white sheets. A long line of shapes under the stained unchanging weight of white sheets.

Look to those who didn't know yet crossed
Look to those who didn't know yet crossed
Look to those who didn't know yet crossed

high / low / steady / truly / desperate / wild / raging / open / wounded / into the fray

Look to those who risked it all to cross
Look to those who risked it all and crossed

)

high / low / steady / daring / humble / wise / open / hearted / into the fray

Excerpt from text and voice cycle
Written for Kim Myhr's collaborative composition
***Pressing Clouds, Passing Crowds* (CD)**

Tim Dooley

–

Diving into *The Waves*

Why is he saying this?
There is birdsong in the wood.
This is the peace you have waited for.
I no longer trouble myself with meaning.
I customize timpani and look out on the moon.
Light comes; light goes; we make light-bulbs you say.
The glassware is taken from the dishwasher and settled on shelves.
They are celebrating some remark about a country house.
A parrot has given the visitors occasion to smile.
There he is, waving his arms at the playpen.
'The case study blocks up the hall.'
The rhythm moves the room.
I say to come.
My opinion is to give.
The statue can be made to talk.
They are celebrating the beat generation.
I am not called upon to gladden my opponent.
There he is, waving his arms at the end of the platform.
The hinge of the world goes golden yet I am not called upon.
She walks towards him, wondering who'll be the first to smile.
In the high season unconsidered words continue to hurt.
A million hands stitch, raise hods with bricks.
The lights come into this room again.
He is there too.
Why is he saying this?
I let the million hands stitch.
A piano has been placed to suggest spontaneity.
There is a history of these meetings, statues, a cinematography.
He wheels his case past strangers, as information is updated.
The golfball was the root of his comeuppance.
Its flight is following the curve of the bay.

The leaves fly because he has passed.
A Life comes and he leaves it open.
Our lake is heaving with fish.
There is no-one behind me.
It blocks up the way.
Headlines are intrusive.
Almost all high gates are iron.
Our long held hopes are frayed.
The kitchen door opens and shuts.
He leaves it open for others to enter.
I leave to others the voice of conviction.
The long afternoon of the service and the served.
Building is moving skyward, heading along the arms of cranes.
The soles of the waitress's shoes sound on the wooden floor.
The state continues to comment on the budget.   )
Some will never come into this room again.
Who else feels stone stairs ache?
The sideways glance.
I too feel the rhythm of Ebbw Vale.
The lightning conductor is worn out.
I am not called upon to give my opinion.
The digitized voice announces unplanned malfunctions.
They are meeting face-to-face in a patisserie next to the Hilton.
So we begin our return to the daily concerns of living.
In the window behind them is continual movement.
But not here, the rag-trade is outsourced east.
Life, life, I told you we have a life.
Is this the voice of possession?
The pope has few clients.
A chief problem is ash.
Hush now.

Philip Hancock

—

Best Route

He knew our cars, the sites we were on,
so he'd park up by the Smallthorne roundabout
in his bronze Chevette and trilby hat.

Slipping off early we'd try the back lanes,
get stuck behind tractors; in side roads
school kids crossed and jostled;
trucks air-horned us joining the A500;
or we'd fret to beat the level-crossing.

Better if we'd hung back – played keepie uppie,
perfected our golf swings – made him hang on
past knocking-off time, waved.

(

Facelift

White gloss we couldn't rag off
her unpruned shrub with turps,
we touched in with undercoats.

It's doing well this year, she said,
returning. Leafless a while since.

The Snow Thing

for Willem van Baalen

within reach of the back door
leant against the wall
where you can get at it.

Worth closer inspection:
two brackets, four screws
clamping an off-cut
of veneered plywood
to a standard brush stale.

It clears your driveway
in no time. Not a spade
or a shovel; let's call it
your snow-shifter – the least
we can do is name it.   )

Sarah Tweed

–

Nando's Super Green Pitta

This is me at 9.15pm on a Thursday, vomiting up my Nando's Super Green Pitta that was supposed to be a wrap but they got my order wrong.

I'm flinging it out of my stomach, through my teeth and into the freshly cleaned bath where my cat sits. He has taken to drinking his water exclusively from there. Flecks of PERi-Salted Chips are spraying onto his whiskers as he looks on with an expression that is hard to decipher. He holds eye contact then does one slow and heavy blink. In the quiet there is a high pitched strumming in the back of my ears that makes it difficult to concentrate. This evening I have discovered a type of shame. A wrenching and twisting humiliation I didn't know I needed to feel. That my body had been used as the punchline of a joke.

Haha: my pale body, bare chested, the raw work of a tattoo artist I had paid to slice into me. A piece that I had chosen and designed to hold me up in moments of self-doubt, crisis, moments like this.

Yet I'm here hurling everything out of my body to make it clean again. Like the bath I am vomiting into. Scrubbed lovingly by my boyfriend who will want to take these dirty feelings into his fists, upper-cutting the nose of the person who made me feel like this. It's good he can't see me now, limpeting onto the side of the bath and won't see me washing my partially-digested self-disgust away. Because this isn't about him.

I'm grasping at fragments of the private, excited discussion I had six months ago with a colleague about the tattoos we were going to get, the artists we had chosen and why. The choices we had made were personal and so were the tattoos. Or mine was. I said as much. His was a large and detailed shoulder piece of an overtly sexualised Native American woman because it 'looked cool' and he didn't believe in cultural appropriation. He believed he, Brooklyn and David Beckham had the right to whatever 'art' they wanted on their bodies. It was their choice.

'That's definitely her', 'her tits are tiny', 'it looks like a prepubescent school boy, chubby in all the wrong places', 'I've seen bigger boobs on a man', 'you couldn't even describe those as jugs, they are more like miniature teacups', 'imagine bringing a girl home only to discover her cans are that small'.

The effort it would have taken to recall the artist I had mentioned. To find her profile, then scroll through six months' worth of images to find me. Everyone around a pub table, preparing to be entertained. Ready for the laugh.

A laughing that abruptly stopped tonight when someone drunkenly recalled the story. Thinking I might laugh too. Like I would join in with the joke. Might become another name on the list of colleagues who had already seen it. Might stand outside of myself pointing and smirking at my own naked body. Like it was just common knowledge. Locker room banter. A bit of fun.

)

Upside Down Rose

I'm writing about the night that we stayed awake picking at the wallpaper of our tiny bedroom. The night when nothing made sense and we talked with our trainers on about whether we should suspend our relationship while we figured out who we were. Or while I figured out who I was. I want you to know I spent the whole of the next week on the Internet, then caught three buses to a tattoo place on Roman Road.

That I crossed black electrical tape over my nipples to conceal their modest and only slightly protruding identity. To stop the men walking to Ladbrokes from getting a thirsty look through the large and brightly-lit window. It didn't of course stop anything, but it made me feel strangely attractive.

The way the artist chatted like nothing was out of the ordinary in her Scottish accent, that she picked up from living with the boyfriend she is now breaking up with. A boyfriend who was perfect and didn't do anything wrong.

Looking at my face, not my exposed chest, she explained, it would hurt like fuck but it would be worth it, and be so beautiful when it was done.

The way I lay on my back and stared hard at drawings of tattoos from those who had been in this exact place before me. I focused on an illustration of a greedy looking centaur whose selfish teeth grinned down at my vulnerable position on the table. I didn't cry then.

The way the artist asked me to hold her tight around the waist and not let go, so she could get the angle just right when she carved, as she called it, right into my lungs.

I am writing this down and not speaking, because I find it hard to explain in my actual voice, without choking on my embarrassment at the thought of how long it's been, that I haven't figured anything out. I'm sorry. But now I have a black flower on my sternum, and that must at least mean something.

Oliver Zarandi

–

Sketches of Boruwlaski: Dwarf; Count

I was neither weak nor puny...

My mother was 67 inches long. My father died when I was nine years old. He was 72 inches long. My mother bore six children, five boys, one girl. Three grew to a normal stature, two of us shorter. One died and did not grow to any height. I stopped growing at the age of four. I remain fixed at 39.6 inches tall. As a child, I was neither weak nor puny. In fact, my mother told me that it was I, Josef Boruwlaski, who was the most taxing upon her vagina.

His head and his heart are equally estimable...

A dear friend, W. Burdon, wrote this about me, on Welbeck Street, London, on May 14, in the year 1818. I am certain my heart is,   )
in size, only as big as a haggis, but it is, in terms of emotions, large and brimming. I have loved many people in my life, many things. Many people, too, have loved me. Perhaps, though, for the wrong reasons. I have been told I dance with the lightness and ease of an opera performer. I have also been told I have the face of a scared child, legs like two twigs.

Bebe

It was on my visit to Lunéville that a jealous court dwarf by the name of Nicholas Ferry (also known as Bebe) picked me up from behind and threw me into a fireplace. I was not burnt. Bebe was thus taken by the people of the court and subsequently whipped. He also received a spanking upon his buttocks which, I am sure, left his cheeks somewhat rouged.

The Old Superstition

If you see a dwarf during your pregnancy, it is said that you will give birth to one. My mother recalls no such thing. 'I did, however,' she said, 'see many tall people, people as tall as oak trees. They were also made of wood.' I do not think my mother knew what she was saying. I loved her, nonetheless.

My violin...

Was given to me as a gift. I plucked its strings with my fingers. This was wrong, I realised. I discovered the bow and slid it across the strings and made sweet music emanate from the wood. In later years, I could not have done what I did without the help of Miss Margaret Metcalfe. I love her dearly.

(

The Turkish...

Are far superior to the Arabians (diary excerpt).

I was taken with illness...

We travelled through Turkey, through the deserts of Arabia. We arrived in Damascus and I was taken with an illness. I was tended to by a Jew, a most worthy man. My body, at this time, felt small and every breath I inhaled and exhaled felt insignificant. My lungs rattled, as if there were marbles rolling inside of me. My illness was assuaged by placing warm cloths across my forehead. I do not know why. In my hallucinatory state, I saw a tortoise. The tortoise was stood on its four legs, its shell large and proud. We spoke, but I do not remember about what exactly. The tortoise said if you think you are ill, then think of my family. An Italian scientist, apparently, had removed the brain of his father. His father lived for some six months more without a brain. I was amazed by this and, as I lay there sweating, I was apparently clapping very slowly, as if in a trance.

What would I do?

Without the love of my protectress? Miss Margaret Metcalfe. Where did they live? A house in Bury St. Edmonds. On a gloomy day, Miss Metcalfe would be a ray of sunshine.

Bread pudding...

It was on my travels across the world that I came to stay at an inn in Birmingham. The innkeeper was a man whose face looked like minced beef. Have you, sir, I said, been attacked recently? He did not hear me because I spoke to his knees. He handed me the food menu and I said, it is Lent, therefore I can only consume bread pudding. For 3 days and 3 nights, I ate bread pudding. I ate so much that all I could say was bread pudding for days afterwards. How are you, Josef? they asked. Bread pudding. Josef, I am sick, can you please pass me some water? Bread pudding. Josef, is your heart aching for a woman? Bread pudding.   )

A Black Cat...

In Soho, a cat entered at my window. I was, at this time, at the height of my fame, if one could call it that. I could play for any audience. The cat was confident. I enjoyed its plump, black body. I ran my hand through its fur. However, the cat was found guilty of murdering several, expensive birds. It was hanged.

A French Soup

My life is filled with small humiliations. Is life, after all, not a series of humiliations? I admit, my English at the time was not perfect, but I understood its sounds. A young woman, with whom I spent some quality time, bid me a good evening and promised to send up Mirabeau. Mirabeau, the celebrated musician. Dead. Believing they would send up his brother instead, I told my servant not to admit him. I did not want to see him after what had happened all those years ago. I heard a rapping on my door. The Impudence, I thought, of this servant. I hid. A servant came in carrying a soup. I jumped out from my hiding place and asked them what this was all about. The servant said, here is your Frenchman, put into a soup dish. *Marrow bone*. The servant walked off laughing, as I slurped up this misunderstanding.

I perceived at some distance...

A man riding upon an ass.

Three words I treasure, that I keep in my pocket...

Jalap. Rhubarb. Laudanum.

(

Another treasure...

My friendship with Miss Metcalfe. I keep the idea of her in my pocket, too, for a rainy day. But will there be a woman who, not as benefactress, but lover, will keep me in her pocket? And I in hers?

O'Brien...

There were several Irish giants roaming Britain. There was one called O'Brien. The public wished to see us together. Brilliant contrasts. It was in public that people gathered around us. I did not reach his knee. O'Brien, 100 inches tall. He put his hand out to shake mine. I wanted him, perhaps, to crush me with his hand, which would have been like me crushing a pigeon in mine.

Wife!

I found a woman and she did indeed fall for me. We were wed. We had children. The life of travelling across the world for my concerts wearied her. She told me she was too sick to come out in London to see me play. Why, I asked. I am turning into a dog, she said. Indeed, I looked closer. Whiskers. A tail. To which I answered? Bread pudding.

Humiliations, oh!

To stand in front of an audience and to be laughed at. One man threatened to put me in his pocket, feed me to the dogs. Another man promised to split me in two with his penis. Etc.

In old age...

I have seen the world. In old age, I treasure my wife, but she, too, is slowing down. My knees click and my arms do not extend fully. I will never bowl again.

)

Miss Metcalfe

Has passed. I had not seen her in a great many years, and I wished to see her before this tragic illness befell her. I do not remember her face, entirely. I can see her eyeball now, wet, glinting in what seems to be the sunlight of my mind. I shall keep her in my pocket, just in case.

Death

Comes to us all, like wind greeting us when we open a door.

Otis Mensah

—

[insert sleep here]

I know you're tired
I've drunk the dry sip that never meets satisfaction
during glimpses I've felt decades of drought
I know all about the boulders that rest in wrinkles
forcing crooked smiles
I know the mass of moons in orbit rest on your weary back
I know how weight feels
I know the cliché that pressure makes for precious stones
but sometimes
sometimes we just break
we break before we meet esteem
still-births still happen to those born and grown

I'm standing on the back of an insect
and in all my power
I found all my insignificance
how life can just be stamped out

I remember the feeling
like cities raining down on my body
drops of water concentrated with people
buildings
iron curtains
time
metal debris
all this world's ills and its machinery
toppling down on my bare back

I know drowning makes it hard to stay awake
I thought about how to think
when your head's trapped in a tank of running water
but your body roams free
I remember gulping and gasping for help

but no one could break me out of myself
I was an insect too
I know how to forget to sleep
and when I keep my eyes open long enough
I see technicolour that isn't there

I stood on the neck of an arachnid
I felt what it feels to have no bones
no structure
just the space in between everything before and after

I know you're tired
I remember the feeling of helpless daze
I remember that sacrifice isn't always compromise

)

Aaron Kent

—

In the Span of Five Hours

We've wrapped the horse in blessings
from the Arctic's snow-driven tide,
in tune with frequencies you and I
can only hear when you are perpendicular
to the wash of insulation and mist.
L'hippocampe is in our midst,
my heart is in the back of its throat
and you appreciate the gesture.

These lights are visitors we ignore
like the unwavering peculiarities
        of our trans-lingual futures.
I draw a straight line from hospital
corners, carrying a tape measure
and your stomach in centimetres.
Each notch is another day's wait
marked in kilohertz and graph paper.

(

I draw stethoscopes on heart monitors
and lean into the curtain to calm us.
We have the shimmer of youth
and the interruption of morning dew
to guide us back to our heavy home.
We tear through names as if burning
        the span of our wings.
And you think you like Lazarus.

Feralism 101

In the event horizon of a cull,
they'll paint us black and white
leach us across tuberculosis'

sympathetic face. Set like milk
marked wide from eye to eye,
they'll coax us feverish within

the soil, bludgeon the fat
reserves from our winter sleep.
They won't let us flea least concern

that we are; enviable scavenge
dig the home we love, sleep
rob the rain pitter pattered worms.

We do not spread neat on bone   )
ash like cattle, tyre torn salt
lick speed bump, intestines

worked over the face of an
open moon. We are cete heavy
in foddered abundance.

What's One Death

I had seen his bedside manner
    More often than not, and learnt
How he crashed into bed like
    A lighthouse batters the ocean
In glare. Their howls phonetic
    In the sustenance of each other,
A canopy between them of
    Linen and lint. He would wake
With the appetite of a wolf,
    Creep into the rayburn warmed
Kitchen, and murder a cub for
    It's voice, to cry for a fuller moon.

(

Mark Goodwin

–

Warm Glow-Ball

a world washed with ice   berg settings this is
not   my mind the click   of ice at it slips
this blue globe from   outer place   is a ball

blue holding a   light bulb with   in in   the
black boot   of my car of some   things
vaguely as they are not   stealing   from the

animals is like biting   at trees' trunks for
nutrition the mind digests not   all its fed
scientific discourse grows really big with

in a plump bouncing   tit   sinister statistics
about lizards & frost   bitten African children   )
the click of ice as it slips the blue of a   blue

globe as blue as the   blue of   blue lips   just
before   a pocked lip of dislocation   just be
fore the smel   ting of images & nations   a

melting of   imagination   we drew in   char
coals you   of me & me of   you our footprints
and believed   in internally lit blue eternally

from   beyond don't   even go there   ham
mer the mortgaged messiah to a white slice of
solid water   with icicles for nails as the bright

sun   light makes   kuh-chink   sounds all around
won   duh   about our species' children's kids but
wonder within & withon   a blue globe   sucked

a big blue gobstopper in the galaxy of a   gob a
solar hole full   this is not   mine mind   the click
of ice as it slips   this blue globe from out   place

is a ball   of blue   a lightbulb in   a black a black
boot switch   slowly the ivy on the globe   is so so
becoming so   stone look   in the dark boot of my

va(r)nished   car one giant leap peel   a polar-cap and
enjoy the moment of one   last   snicker this oak
leaf dresses the face of blue sky with my wishes to

kiss the rich   mud & cunt   suds on bonnets in Oz
LEDs glisten amongst dirty or   ganic spuds dot this
blue place round www three seagulls flying up   side

        d   own & cream   ice   warm vacuum

(

Maria Sledmere

—

from *Swerve*

II.

> This motion on the page is analogous to that of the swimmer
> who takes pleasure in the act that also saves her from drowning
> — Roan Retallack, *The Poethical Wager*

I swerve in the sacrifice zone of myself.
No tossed rituals of turmeric, the year we all wrote
fairest of frost and I forgot to whittle my nails.
So it was deep inside you: droplet of soap,
slash invective in the stream.
Sky gets pink. One of three
mentions includes 'legit' and you try to speak
and the box upturns assorted sweets.
A cumulus nuclear foam of news, a chorus   )
soldered. What comma, unnecessarily
frail of bone and the hungering water.
If you could just learn to appreciate the trees
   like a box tick
forests are indifferent
to those who sing inside them, can you hear
the feinting coil and a lyrical split.

Getting sober again. We slay avocado
light estranged. Optative
verse for the monstrous among us, one
of our kin must burn. I caught you kissing
the end of the sentence, becoming pith.
   It meant big things like possession
and the mirage of Fire Island was only
pink light on the opposite window
   from which you saw a solar figure.

It glyphs for the literal measure.
These static missives; I was in the daylight,
undecided. How did you not get hungry.
I was an Alice, an Icarus.
I watched you clawing green meat
from the skin of a memory, slipping
just so in a similar bed
   would I unlock the all in reverse?
   Your breath was oceans in my ear
and so—

   III.

The numbers, such as they were
could not correspond to a season. Autocorrect the liminal
with your gelatine print, portfolio sales. In such cloud
as this anaphylactic blackness, you have been stung
so many times as to wither the government.
   Fuck the autumn weather, the plenitude of stems
and lyric apples; fuck everything in the menagerie now
you can't get up, thorax, stray violin and veering
west to south like air. I wanted a sheer
definition of *lyre*; liar, leer
at the starting scene. Play-press
to collect this, parcel abundance
stuck couriers. I love
you like milk loves milk
before it is sold
a sour war, a platitude.

Dearest appraisal of day in the seam.
Swerve is a move of consciousness
accordant to blue
or nuclear red, internal burn
even prior to cloud; even that
particular snow, so pink it would make

(

a nurse blush to tend the skin
so burnt by it. Pray-less
the village were moving silkier into themselves
in masses of communal water; a drunk man
comes to repair the starling
not far from my father's lodge.

Will you ever have sex again, I ask the crow
who visits my lovely English oak
and spreads its loving black on the green
and swivels around in the wetness
of all that black, shiniest feathers
stirring to melt in the liquid breeze
I see with. The emphasis of moon
has been. Sweet imperilled self again,
we have no use for your atoms
we gather up your bitten dreams.
The crow is cautious.
The crow is a pronoun, don't say   )
the wind in the grass is changing course;
the crow is anachronism.

This is the picture of the lake that was taken.
This is the hungriest daisy, lackadaisical
I am become flower; I swerve in the breeze
which is only the lyric.
Summoning out of syntax.
Close our pretty face at night.
My iPhone detects a faceless ethics
as though I had Levinas on speed dial already
sufficient to ever corrupt the line.
   Baby's cry dot em pee three,
the beneficial empathy, duly served.
Have I said what I have had to say of a swerve
when the car pulled in and almost killed me
quick as a kiss,

redeliver your life.
Touchstone shimmer, eight-bit lyric
carry your nerve in the kissing
be less of the bloom you become
as lace. I tie up loose ends
for you in the hold, enter gravitational
we become apposition. She lets herself
towards becoming less: gives away
her clothes, her sparkling dolls, her cancelled glitter.
They enslave polyethylene terephthalate
in our fish, this literal, it is likely
the glitter will teem in our seas.
I relinquish my hold in eucalyptus cellulose
enhancing 'natural selection'
astride our brazen shine. It is promiscuity,
mutating in quick, November air
as though contact itself were ambient only
where you realise the also in the am
(I are; them are us too
and a late perishing, a curl of protein.

Anecdote is super effective.
Goodbye first love, goodbye, goodbye
I tidy my shoes. You split a lace
and count the elegant swans by the lake
we only painted. Tiny glitter in your eye
was almost blinding. I let my fingers graze
the rocks and leaves, pleading feedback:
Yohuna, Eudaemonia.
The cars tipped over overnight—
   A glass of white wine
and I see the salt-dried oils before me
and google reveals all spent earth in churlish pastels,
as if Camille had not drawn up the plans
and held her own. Desire exists
in the twisted red, susurrations between glass panels

and these exquisite remains of a tree.
   Life is good to know,
a deciduous shot that flares and falls
in the corpus of writing, I forget my aphoristic lust
in message body, crying on my mother's kitchen floor—
five years that have passed, five elisions of summary
in which light at eight is a miracle paragraph
we live by the calyx of online status,
   a singular ovular green
beside the smallest, familiar face.

)

David & Lizzy Turner

—

#1 overhand

the sudden, overwhelming realisation is the
simplest type, is one of the most fundamental
and forms the basis of many others that this
person, this person, This and hence it is
very secure if it is intended to be permanent
to prevent the end of a rope from unravelling
the minds of the pair, by joining the ends
Spills if pulled forcibly in the wrong
(direction This that this person, This is
secured to its own standing part tied up
tightly against, true in the mathematical
sense, and almost impossible to untie without
sudden, overwhelming This this person This
Three different names for what is the same
realisation that this depending on how tight
you need it to be pull to tighten the, This
this person, takes two and ties them together

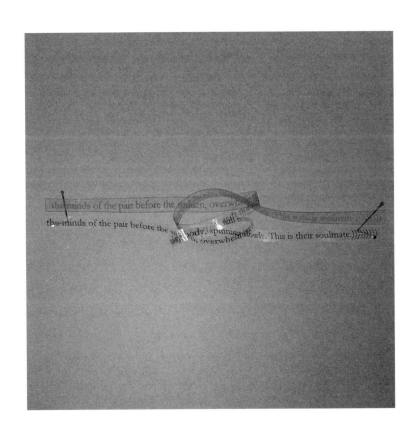

the minds of the pair before the sudden, overwhelming this is their soulmate.

the minds of the pair before the sudden body, spinning overwhelmingly. This is their soulmate.))))))

)

#2 sailor's

(

This is the moulding of a chill before Spun from freezing fog to your windward side of mind The halting of a These vibrations shadow-soft and shaken off Too feathery to cling But floating from a dense rimed bone somewhere within This is the deposit of a translucent spell Made limpid from a screen of vapour To what is introduced This oak table-top These recollections have been brought to their frost point Too flimsy unaided But too clear to shake This is the uncountable plural of formations Winding out of the morning It won't evaporate of course So thick it looks like snow The interlocking splinters attach to What is exposed They may float unaided but that isn't the same as This is the trimming of above and below

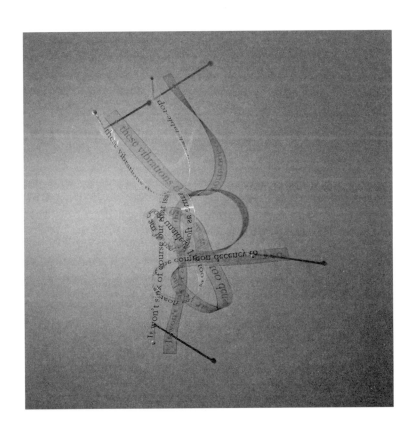

)

Vanessa Onwuemezi

–

Bird Nest

Announcement she made:

'I'm going into the loft to find my equipment. Farewell. Barring rape or murder, I'll be back in not too long.'

I asked him if he'd heard that? He rolled his eyes. 'Yeah, on and on she goes right? Just get on with it without all the chat.'

We conversed as we had been before, settling on subjects that made me uneasy, because they were too real for me to comprehend. I was stupid.

'Anyway…' He was unpacking Tupperware, noisily, he forced his nails under the rim of a large one, opened, threw the lid to the side, and within that, progressively smaller and smaller containers, opened opened. Inside the smallest one at the centre, there was something old, something rotting, covered in dark flattened oval flecks, like thyme leaves.

(

'Argh,' he said, 'fermented crap. Is this where I left it? Was this a good idea? Not edible.' He threw the lot into the kitchen bin, which wasn't covered. The stench lingered. All the cats turned up and hung around. 'Politically, we're fucked, economically bamboozled, climate-wise, the rest remains to be seen. The forecast is sunny straight to hell.'

I walked over to the sink to get some water, after searching in a few of the many wood-panelled cupboards for a glass while he watched. They were tall, a stretch even for me a tall person. The ceiling was double their height and their brass handles too ornate to grip comfortably.

She walked back into the room with a mixer and clunked it down onto the green stone worktop. Dust fell from it like dry ice. Around twenty cats mewed around the bin. She grabbed one of them by its hind legs, pulled it close, rubbing up and down.

'You're so cute I could kill you,' she said, then turned to him. 'I need six eggs, can you get me some? It stinks.'

'Six, for cakes? Sure.' He grabbed his wallet and slid it beneath his arm.

'These will be celebration cakes. Mind those gypsies in the carpark, scum.'

'Do you really mean that?' I said to her.

'Exactly.' He stepped directly in front of her, looking at me with bald eyes. I could feel him breathing. 'Shopping, rape, eggs, no respite,' and he yapped his hand like a duck quacking.

)

Linda Black

–

Her clothes worked well

– stippled vest, ingrained elastic, nurtured bodice, the stent of a full demeanour. A staged game – *her* game. All roads crossed by nature, stalled by lights expending motes. Control, dingbats of caution.

In her were words of difference. Nicked, notched, snatched. She'd carried on. Threadbare. No bike to get on. Simultaneously through school and puberty. Imagine a dead hedgehog. Imagine her bleeding shame. Racemes of it.

The bleeding-heart dove is shy and secretive. The bleeding-heart dove (genus *Gallicolumba*) has a pronounced reddish hue extending down the belly.

(

Char char charcoal – bolts & burns, briars & barnacles. A/bashed. In the snick of the woods, the pike of the lane (predatory with large teeth), the skew of the ginnel, yaw of the byway.

Spittle and grimace. The illusion of blood: post-box, signal-box, fire-engine, guts. No back-up, no back-drop, no back-chat –*bone* –*stab* –*slap* –*lash* –*bite* –*hand* –*story*. Blackout.

Scarper

Before I bag you. Formerly there were places to hide – cabins, balaclavas, mine-shafts, blankets. States of retribution. I ran away, came back, held my own hand. Drought slipped through my finger nails. I and they had to grow.

One single thing is impossible. A saucer, a quart of curdled milk (too true); mashed potato (just the one).

Significant suppers. The road torched. Scram, head for the hills. However one tried. Russian Vine. A rhyme for forgot. Make yourself scarce.

Personality peers. Bumps, lumps, traits... given to me. Lips of balm, Sellotape, unrequited gratitude.

Remove the skin and innards. Stuff the neck. Before proceeding check the weather vane – are the neighbours arguing/making amends?   )

Blot squat begot; swat plot snot; dry-rot mug-shot; job-lot liver-spot pain-pot; knot slot blud-clot Scapa Flow (go) skedaddle. The burglars legged it before the police showed up. The ship leaves at midnight.

Claire Crowther

—

Goddess, She of Surprising

Opening the bedroom door and there, Her, kneeling.
Her pointing
at the blue pattern looping through orange wool:
'You're the one
to explain this. Your metaphors.' Me, speechless.
My husband
in bed, reading. His recognition of Me, His accepting
woven stuff.
The slack of a sports page. Crackling. His hands steepling
like prayer
guides. He gasping at the door seeing a goddess standing
holding cups,
welcoming Us to Our day off, the relaxing of what comes
at the end
of the week of Me buying a rug. (Our bed being high. Me falling.
Rugs holding
pain.) Me seeing Her leaning on the door frame as He is seeing Her.
Me kneeling
wiping up water spilling on tufts bending under rushing knees and feet.
We being
sustainable. Me thinking: Are we Being electrons, the One electron
shooting back
and forth in time? No, walking on, One Being. There Being
Others in
Us, making Our Whole. My feet freezing. She on Her haunches.
Looking at
what I am looking from. Her big eyes. My tough chin. His praising.
Me getting
into bed. A streak of blue pushing in from the glazing-out. Morning.

Puff

I wish you would exaggerate enough
to make morefulness of things
all fuller than you think

your woods are empty of puffed shapes your leaves
aren't stuffing up such thick sun
as the purple pigeons

on your fence need to plump your thin words
can't swell encumbered and
perhaps I should expand

I wish you would at least overdo thoughts
of 'let's have less *or*' and
'up the *and*' here to hand

is extraness coming UFOs   )
burst through big cloud let dearth
be now dismissed on earth

nor beam your blaze of light on binaries
nor whisper thoughts of 'just dust'
nor the concrete 'never'

Donya Todd

—

Parallel voyage

(

My wife and I,
sailing from the strange islands,
slipped into the warm. Filling and formed.
Our last voyage over the grey waves.

I felt a different man, but she suffered nightmares of huge seas.
She was my wife – she was a 3 in tenseness
and 4 in bitter enmity.

The dimensions of my daughter
took more definite shape.
She asked: 'When shall we get ashore, daddy?'

The most awful yellow-green sunrise. A dream of Hell.
The rain was black, hissing and boiling, a seething sea.
Cold despite the sun.

I spun her around.
She at sea with her menfolk, kept pretty
like a blunt knife. A sweet-heart,
taking the waters the whole time.

)

Jim Jones, the Commander's son. She had swept
him overboard and he had broken a bone in his hand.
The synchronisation of forms.

She was perfectly happy. There was nothing more we could do.
The hurricane warped the feeling storm –
A thrumming extra-frictional cyclone.

The foaming pyramid
Rose above the mountains.
Six pleasure vessels were sunk.
She sailed on, in a grey world of her own.

A man and his wife,
Sea-sick on the disorder of mis-placed particles,
make errors of exactitude.

The two of them heaved on the long warp,
Aware of the tripping line.
They discovered the truth:
There was nothing.

Theodoros Chiotis

–

Caesura:abscission

one   can
          not
 find any
        thing
    here that
     does not
     smell like
    an
       nihilation

this confluence
 of crows
    a murmuring of mouths
 a murderful grudge
(a necrophilic advance
  a drooping of wings

a reminder of the significant
 difference between grief and
 reconnaissance:
     now is the time to
learn
     about predators one must avoid.

*

The claim to sovereignty
as one descends into the grave carrying
two keys
       one in each hand: a sign of iniquity
the cast of the body
of a guard dog
 discovered in a
    Pompeiian domus.

Said body of said guard dog
contorted beyond any chance
of escaping the
 time-of-times-already-gone.

The call
to oblivion
persists.   A body un
                recognisable
the collar chain
keeping
            everything in
place.
The angel never arriving in time
to roll away the stone

)

Every morning

Every morning
black milk spills out of my body
    the world
                               gooey
dripping from the side
   of my head

an incursion into
   reality.

Once I had more death be
                           tween my
fingers. The spring solstice
 fails to bring
   forth new earths.

The fire at the altar an attempt
to sleep with the palms of night
buried deep into the lake
of the spleen.

Our bodies now gravel
at the feet of Gorgo,
   argonaut flesh
never to be sacrificed.

And what of the poem?
            The poem
            now
a machine to keep the body alive
     with words that only sever
          connections and show
there is nothing but the whistle
coming out of the holes in trees.
Porous with pain
  my mouth tastes of berries.
There is nothing here but pores and

(

every pore is a void
    and every void is the result of poor manufacturing of the material used
and every void is generally deemed undesirable
and every void affects the mechanical properties and lifespan of the body
and every void also acts as a crack initiation site
allowing moisture to penetrate the cladded body.

Let me reiterate this: voids are considered defect.
I have worked hard at not becoming a void. What is the use in being a
honeydew deformity?
So I drink black milk –
    this way you won't be able to see that
my body does not flow in the way it should.
You can only see black where there should be light passing through.

They are now growing cotton on the surface of the moon
and knitting wool now is used as padding for the body;
    any excess threads simply flow out of the hole that used to be the mouth.
What do I gain by not dying?
What is it that I am completing which is by design decaying and failing?   )
The weight of cattle bred for food exceeds the weight of free animals.
What does it mean to be a body amongst other bodies?
The black mould spreads, the body is perfected while rejecting what
Are perceived as fault lines.
What happens when
you ex(cor)cise the stolen pieces?
What gets left behind?

The other night I found a letter with a date marking my death;
the date being closer to the present than I am comfortable with means
I have to live with that date.

When I saw my grandfather's lungs
they looked marbled
  they were in the acute
stage and the blue
areas of consolidation
looked like the sea.

(from *a sentence*)

Susannah Dickey

—

oranges and oranges and oranges

Orange?

What?

Would you like an orange?

Oh. Sure.

The woman in a red gilet and a beige short-sleeved shirt hands you an orange. You start to peel it, but the peel comes off in barely perceptible fragments, like pencil rubbings or dandruff. The orange seems to stay as one unimpeachable whole, only now it's a bit wet. You look around, sticky-fingered. There's an inch of windowsill invisible behind a bus-coloured curtain. You set the orange down, retreat. Your misdemeanour is immediately invisible. The cabin reeks of oranges. You try to follow the smell, but it's like trying to follow a mirror reflected in another mirror. Everywhere is humid with orange.

You edge your way around a group of people in a circle, past a ficus plant the height of a wardrobe; you step over a bucket with an inch of pale wet inside.

Have you heard anything yet? The voice arrives behind you.

Oh, you say. You'd forgotten, actually. *No,* you say, *Haven't heard anything yet. You?*

Me neither, he says. He has thick hair down to his shoulders and when you press your face into it you feel like a small Toyota in a drive-through car wash.

Cool, you say.

Bit weird this, isn't it?

Orange you glad we came?

He laughs, then stops. *Did we?* he says.

A woman handed me an orange, you say.

Me too.

What did you do?

What do you mean what did I do — I ate it.

How?

I sold my hair to a passing salesman in exchange for an orange peeling comb made of the finest ivory.

Oh.
With my hands and then my mouth, that's how I ate it.
Oh.

There's a plastic tablecloth-d table decorated with oranges, prepared in different ways. A sausage-length sheet of cardboard has 'Buffet' written on it in gurgled handwriting. There are orange segments perforated with cocktail sticks and oranges hidden under blankets of milk chocolate. *Although I suppose there could be anything under there* he says. *Four grapes in a chocolate trench coat* you say. *Grapes trying to sneak into an R-rated film* he says. There's a salad with skin-coloured cous cous and black olives and shredded, gossamer orange and pomegranate seeds. There's a charred-looking orange, just blossoming, covered in tahini. There are orange slices with sliced up boiled potatoes and orange slices in a fruit salad and orange slices stuck to the sides of chalky meringues, like slugs.

I'm not sure this counts, you say, picking up a segment on cocktail stick.

How come?

It's hardly a method of preparation.

So if I stuck a fork into you would you not call that a serving suggestion?

I'm not sure I'd be able to call it anything through all the screaming.

At least your juices would run clear.

He takes a ladle-full of tabbouleh and you peel the segments off a bulb of meringue and crunch into its cartilage. Detritus floats to the floor. The two of you leave a trail as you walk to the Bobbing For Oranges stand and then to the stand where people are throwing oranges at stacked pins for prizes. The woman in the red gilet is roving lazily, like a September wasp. She offers her plate to a triumvirate of oily men, already holding plates piled high with food. They shake their heads and she moves on.

Why is she even bothering with that? he says.

Maybe she takes pride in her work, you say.

Ugh, he says, *Imagine.*

No thank you.

You meander, finally landing equidistant between two groups. You're wearing enormous trousers with furry pockets and he regularly strokes them, which is what you wanted. A woman to your left is relaying an incident from her past. She has her back to you and you can see that the zip on her dress isn't the whole way up, but her hair is soft-looking.

That weekend we took a friend's dog for a hike. We stopped at the top and let her off the leash. We sat down, had some water. Connie, the dog's name was. She was sniffing all about the place, the way dogs do. She was old, maybe. She couldn't see so well, maybe. She lay down, started rolling about. She rolled off.

Rolled off what? a man with a small mouth asks.

Rolled off the mountain.

Oh my god.

We found her, hours later. It was dark by then. She was all bent.

That's horrible.

We had to carry her home wrapped in a jacket. She was stiff as an ironing board.

(

You turn to him, to see if he heard what you just heard, but his focus is on the other group of people. You adjust, to hear what he's hearing. A woman with wide hair and the kind of skin that looks like it is licked regularly by a horse is talking. She smiles at you, but doesn't pause.

And so, she says, *One night I go to bed – and I didn't bother to lock my door, because that's just not how we did things. I wake up some time in the night and sit up. I notice my friend from the bunk next door – Amy – sitting under the desk next to my bed. She's all scrunched up, folded like a sofa bed or an accordion, and she's just looking at me. She had these big eyes and all this long, black hair, and she's just sitting there, staring. I say, 'Amy, mate, you alright?' It was hard to speak because I'd just woken up and the air in the cabins used to get so cold and constrictive at night, remember? Anyway, she doesn't reply. I turn my phone on to check the time – it's like, 3am – and I have a message from her. It says, 'Fliss, I can't sleep, so I'm going to come sit with you.' She did this sometimes – she had real bad insomnia. God,* she pauses to take a forkful of roast orange with yoghurt, *The food this year is incred, right? Anyway, so I say, 'Amy, mate, you don't have to sleep on the floor. Why not just get in the bed with me?' but she still says nothing, just keeps staring at me with those big eyes, so eventually I figure whatever, I'll leave her to it, so I roll over and go back to sleep. Little while later, I wake up again, turn, and she's still there. No, no, seriously, I swear. Still there, still watching me. I check my phone again and it's about 4. I unlock it, and the text message from earlier is gone. I check my log to see if I just accidentally deleted it from my inbox, but no. No text. Seriously, I hadn't received a text that night – must have dreamt that Amy had texted me. But I look up from my phone, and, yep, yep, I swear, there's still someone, something, sitting under my fucking desk, watching me. Floor-length black hair, eyes like fucking cauliflowers, blank expression. So,* Fliss shrugs, *Yeah, I figured, right, this is it – this is how I die. There's a damn demon under my desk and it's going to eat me, or whatever. I resign myself to death. And so, I watch it for a while, and it watches me, and sooner or later, I don't know, I guess I fall asleep. Wake up, nothing there. I spoke to Amy after; she hadn't set foot in my cabin. Weird, right?* She takes another forkful of orange. *Seriously,* she moans, *This stuff is unbelievable. Who don't you put those damn suitcases down, Pam, and eat some fucking food?*

)

You can feel him touching the furry pannier on your right hip and your breath catches a little. You look at him and he gestures with his head at the woman standing opposite you. You turn, and notice that the woman is holding a suitcase in each hand.

Pam, is it? you say, and she looks at you like how she might look at someone with a dachshund in a buggy. *Why the –?* you say, and you let your fingers twirl in the direction on the suitcases.

It's so I can have my arms up, later, Pam says, like it's obvious. You feel the air around you get shaked by his noiseless laughter.

Makes sense, he says, still quivering. You put your elbow into him. You nod at Pam, try to look supportive. Fliss offers her a chocolate ball and she leans forward and bites into it. Juice courses down her chin and stays there, wet and permanent like veins in a marble slab. Nobody says anything for a moment. From somewhere behind you there is the occasional tulip-y echo of a glockenspiel.

Hey. Hey. You two. The two of you turn, and the woman in the gilet is there. *Did you hear?* she says.

Hear what? you say.

Have you heard yet, I mean, she says.

Oh. You'd forgotten again.

No, he says. *We haven't heard anything.*

Check your emails, she says. *Have you been checking your emails?*

No, you say. *I've had my data turned off.*

I like the way you say data, he says.

Data, you say.

Data, he says.

Data! she says. *That's so funny!*

We'll check now, he says, and you bring out your phones.

Oh, you say.

What? What is it? he says, still coaxing.

I won, you say.

Shit! he says, and finally his phone complies. *Shit – I won too,* he says.

(

I know, the woman in the gilet says, and she brings out from the pocket of her gilet two envelopes. Fliss is holding a cake. It could be a carrot cake; a carrot and orange cake. Everyone is watching. The glockenspiel plinks louder and more often.

We won, he says.

We won, you say.

I'm glad you're here, he says.

My name is Gemma, by the way, the woman in the gilet says. She oscillates her smiling face. The room smells like after a hockey match.

Miruna Fulgeanu

–

La Quinta del Sordo

*The Quinta del Sordo (English: Villa of the Deaf), or Quinta de Goya, was the name of an
extensive estate and country house situated on a hill in the old municipality of Carabanchel
on the outskirts of Madrid. The house is best known as the home of Francisco de Goya in the
years leading up to his exile, and where he painted the Black Paintings comprising fourteen
murals. Contrary to popular belief, the estate was given its name due to the deafness of a
prior owner, having nothing to do with Goya himself, who was deafened by illness in 1792.*
(Wikipedia)

That there is a time set aside, like a leap year, for you
to get reacquainted with the dark. Wild, that all along
you wanted to be held, so never considered doing
the holding yourself. The frost eats too, you know. Mad,

that trees dieback, a condition of woody plants that have lost
touch with their peripheries, agreed to come closer to themselves.   )

That in November the air can just drop like that, or how
in 1819 Spanish painter Goya was deaf and purchased
the Quinta del Sordo, implying some things at least are saved
for you. Whirled and windswept, off on a honeymoon

with a ghost troupe, and little but black and ochre
on the palette: the dark of the cypresses, the pollen.

What can you do when all the stairs lead downwards
only? He paints on the walls to keep track of them.
In the dining room, Saturn devours his son, eyes fixed
on a table with one chair. That it's been so long, the candles

have squatted into pyramids of wax. And in this chest of yours,
the fear lies down, horizontal, having
finally settled, like snow. You have to trust

The Dog

Oil mural on plaster. 131.5cm × 79.3cm. It shows the head of a dog gazing upwards.
The dog itself is almost lost in the vastness of the rest of the image, which is empty
except for a dark sloping area near the bottom of the picture.
(Wikipedia)

Wasn't this your long-held suspicion – that the end is all
eyes, waking together? Asking at this late hour, it's all so easy
to take apart. True, on his deathbed, asked if he still wanted
anything before his life was out, Juan Miró said
TAKE ME TO THE DOG. But when the earthquake came for you,
it asked its questions in the invisible half
of the world, while you, sitting cross-legged
by a ceiling-high terracotta stove, took on
its waves, seeing if you could count its Richter degrees
on the fingers of one hand. The terracotta clattered,
but nothing else would give away – only the ground
grinding out madrigals as you sank into the bed:
cheap plush in which to wait, nest, rest; to see
which way the silence comes. To what end
would you keep pity, when the earth
has always had such swallowing powers.
Listen out, hunch over
and try to look this dog
straight in the face.

(

Lotte L.S.

–

Affection for cave, single watt

as certain as there is cum on the pillowcase
she could not   see to see

it took single cell
it took near-finished syllables
it took the crimson-blue fact
it took if not the exact colour the exact shape
it took without appearing at all
it took all goddamn night

the harder we try the harder it is to remember

how the trees stood like   YYYYYY
unravelling repairs she made by night

)

'there was no scientific precedent for leaving
people together in the dark'

tranquillity vs. the absence of violence
the consequence of love on the page

the doppelgänger looked just like him   but saw lime-green not crimson-blue
gave in easy to her requests   as a palm opening to its bride
dazzling clusterfuck of fingers   reminding her
anything would get wet if you were prepared to throw water at it

now the foreground is beyond us
just dismantling the forever

the sky's answering machine
like, busy \ out making, like, plans to end it all
    like, booking hotel rooms, like,
karaoke with, like, wireless headphones, like,   a rope / a rope

large enough for like the whole fucking sky to slip through

and the lyric waited
for the lyricism to begin

waking up to sightless dreams
waking up to the unification of an all-you-can-eat government
          the mouth trying to emulate the whole sorry face
\ the overbearing elegance of the stalagmites   just blaring in the free air

the generous highway on fire
the highway generously on fire

waking up to charlotte's mouth   the future of no-future
waking up to an idea that became t-h-e idea
waking up to plastic hangers dressed in something altogether more terrifying
woke up in colour memories / o blue,   arise
or, like,   it could have been lime-green
(
          woke up to!
the sensation of the room taking off
fruit sweeter than ever before

whole glades of fingers
hugging her insides
she put her ears to its desires   one fat fist in an open-air cell

and the lyrical thought
was deemed pleasurable and so unpublishable

then the syllable spoke for itself
then night unravelled through the trees
then this is no kind of forever
then the language forgot transcendence   like,
a cockroach in the dark / like, Signs of Concern / like, sitting in sickbay
watching everyone else play ball
then the sky called 999 from its hotel room   'overdosed on blue'
          the trees refusing to assist

layer-cake-like atrium   sky ready to fling itself over the sorry stairs
then the light evaded a use
then the soul remained terrifically unstirred

'j'en ai assez'   the lyric no longer had the right to remain quiet

the stalagmites began to drop in succession
finally then the palm tasted the free air
then the present came ever closer
then my sweet little doppelgänger
then my sweet little doppelgänger
then the thought came strongest
        periodically turning on the light
then it touched the fact:

never around   but through
through but   never around

)

Synapses, between

Thereafter   there were shadows grazing the sugar granules
artificial limelight consoling every picture frame

swallows lived underground during winter

the trees work against themselves   splendid bitches
naïvely ironing their suits

looking forward to becoming a toddler two hundred years from now

when the person in the photograph   is I seven years from now
this spring   I grew half an inch

I will be gone before I is seven years from now   birthdays
of conkers sinking pockets

(anniversaries
of expired feelings   laters, mwah

there is another world   but it is outside this one
when you spoke everything in the room just disappeared for me

when everything   how do we

what I found underneath was moss I took out my pocketknife
reluctant to abandon my dead   my one consolidating death

a part of   how it helped me to see

I don't mind g-o-d but I don't care for his groundsmen
the imperfect o   of their knees

o   I am so thankful for the seeing

Gareth Evans

–

Priority Status

Oh, it's such a perfect day
I'm glad I spent it with you*

There are two tiers, no, stages of architecture in the current light:
the nearer lower brown brick buildings, and the further, taller, soft
steel, slate-blue towers. The latter could be characters out of a Melville
mid-century *policier*. (He is now seen distinct, a maker of prescient
greatness: cinema's poet of restless waiting, of the so often empty
world.) They seem to have soaked up a little of the sky, any haze of
which is now entirely meteorological, climactic, after weeks stripped of
airborne and earthbound traffics. They stand over the sprawl, feeling
closer than they are; their ennui however, differently tempered, not
a Melvillean melancholy of the empty, shuttered villages of France;
at least not now. Later, who knows... when the sun changes its clothes,
angles slant and we lean into sunset's gleam; difference visible in   )
different light. There's always something more behind the seen.

For now, abiding warmth and the year accelerating spring into summer's
steeper heat. Dogs and cats lying on their own flanks across the cooler
stone and slabs; symmetrical, like half animals waiting to be opened
into fuller being; how we made those hanging angel decorations, and
what simple magic it was to cut the folded, only to open a holey whole.
You can wear the afternoon. Do children still focus their magnifying
glass into a burning paper point, an eclipse of energy, discover the
elemental excitements; do they even have them, know them anymore,
the tool? Perennial pleasures lost when we were looking somewhere
else, for something now forgotten, down the fading years.

Oh, such a perfect day...

So the question, dormant, never gone, but retreated under like a kernel
in winter ground, has with the season's shift climbed once again to the
surface of the turning mind...

'There's a beautiful story about the Russian poet Anna Akhmatova. Her son was arrested during the Stalinist purges. One day, she was standing outside the prison with hundreds of other women in similar situations. It's Russian-cold and they have to go there every day, wait for hours in this big open yard, then get the answer that, today and every day, there will be no news. But every day they keep coming back. A woman, recognizing her as the famous poet, says, "Poet, can you write *this*?" And Akhmatova thinks about it a second and goes, "Yes."'**

Priority (n.) late 14c: 'state of being earlier', from Old French, from Medieval Latin: 'fact or condition of being prior', from Latin; from *c.*1400 as 'precedence in right or rank'.

...how to live...

We wait to cross the road, wait for the green 'man' walking, although there are no cars. We wait for the tone of emptiness to change. Is this something poignant, a harking back to how it was, some small wish to return; return to what, recover what, a form of transport that scythes down millions, makes toxic the common morning, heats the large hall of earth, buries the green under the grey.

...how not to die, without first having lived, so far from purpose that purpose makes no sense...

I am made whole by my scars***

what is seen is not / what is there / what is heard is not / what is there / not enough of / what is there / so narrow our spectrum skills / how much we miss / of the universe so made / how much we do not find / that matters then and still

Light is matter. The intangible is tangible. Hope and resistance are forms of matter: they can be seen; they can be heard. They slip in and out of reception like deer: look and listen, cross the road to join them.

'He returned to New York, where he took a few short-lived teaching jobs, including one at CW Post College. *He told me that he was forced to quit for passing all of his students, who faced conscription to the war in Korea if they could not pass their classes.* It was Samuel's experiences in war that most informed his philosophy, simply to live each day as if it were the last.' ***

...how to find the measure / how / where is it held...

'Living and writing for some 50 years in a walk-up tenement in Greenwich Village, he sat at a modest window-facing desk until the sun rose beyond the rooftops across Thompson Street, when he headed out into the streets, and eventually to Central Park, where he walked and met with friends until darkness fell.' ***

what is past / passed / on

In 1937, Russian writer Varlam Shalamov, aged 30, was arrested for 'Trotskyite' activities and sent to the hard-labour camps of Kolyma in Siberia (later he would publish his defining 'tales' of this period and place). He remained imprisoned until 1953. The winter temperature often reached minus 60 Celsius. He worked in the goldmines and coalmines, the timber-yards, until he was 'saved' by a doctor and given a job as a camp hospital attendant. He told how the hands that held the pickaxe or spade handles would stay fixed in their curved grip for weeks and months, unable to unclench until the thaw.

)

the everyday ecstatic waits / the boughs of birch / branching light between / the blocks the avenue of cherry / a single maple red / and we walked further / than allowed far / down to the river and / the river met us there

He died aged 75 in a squalid state care home in 1982. The memorial stone of his gravesite was vandalised in the early 2000s, but the planetary body 3408 Shalamov, discovered and named for him in 1977, continues to circle the sun.

Pain is not a marketplace. Pain should not be a marketplace.
There are numerous ways the body can give up; or not give up.

...how the desired life has slipped out of reach / or sight / or taste...

Imagine the small hands: their blossoming in time.

blood from the nose / as instant as the turning / to a sound and back /
the opening of a rose / who knows why / perhaps the brain is weeping /
for all / it cannot change

There is a loft at 141 Wooster Street, NYC. In it is the *Earth Room* of
Walter de Maria. It has been there since 1977. It contains 250 cubic yards
of earth. It covers 3,600 square feet. It is 22 inches deep and weighs
280,000 lbs. It is an earth room on the earth. It moves through space.

young / at any age / the rustle of the pages / can sound / like kindling /
a small fire / world as it is / and might be / opening / out of print

(

Simone Weil died in 1943, aged 34, in Ashford, Kent, emaciated after
months of reduced nutrition, living in solidarity with the Occupied
workers of the France she longed to return to.

...how the dream of a life is itself a privilege...

'Priest holes' still exist in many English country houses. Designed to
provide temporary refuge in times of persecution, they were situated
beneath floors, in hollowed walls, false chimney spaces. Created to
stop death in its stalking tracks, they were not shaped for comfort,
but harsh necessity.

...how to write from inside the necessary reason...

In the years immediately preceding his death, aged 29, in 1993, the artist
Absalon made a number of sculptural 'living quarters' he called *Cellules*.
These were spaces proportioned to his body, designed for daily need, each
different, each white, and each intended for installation in a different city.

/ There are people who are determined by certain registers of means to have no value who are without enduring worth now or then or any day to come who are cast aside they stumble through the corridors of transport on repeat repeatedly ignored they fall on down the carriage into their terminal time and in the air behind them leave a trace of present ghosts /

John Berger once observed that the work to make a cup is only the beginning of the labour associated with that vessel. How many thousand times will it be served, washed, put away...

Strangely welcome the singular threat it seems, the grouped focus, microscope attention, while above us, through the daily cleaner skies, the constellated stories shine and flare, their signal fires, gazing down on the joined up myriad of risks that nobody can speak to with urgency or scale, not enact an adequate response...

Imagine archaeology in visible time, the layered experience given shape and formal pressure now.

)

still late in nights / in finance squares piazzas / and arcades the dark / graffitis warnings over chrome / and glass that only / nighthawks read

I grew up with a recurring dream of constriction between huge ill-defined shapes. I would push my toys down into the crevice between settee cushions. I suffered from hay fever and occasionally asthma. The primal fear is of an 'oubliette'. I think often of the waking bells fitted in Victorian graveyards. I have only seen *The Vanishing* once. I am not drawn to latex.

Touch
Watch
Walk
Read
The Risen Bread of Friendship
Note
How the Light Consorts
With Evening Trees

we are coated / in the fast shadows of the / birds that are still left / that have not left / quite yet / we are not bereft / quite yet

Under conditions of pressure and panic things fossilise into fixity or become torrent fluid. Those who are un-housed shelter in the larger of the bins. There is no making for posterity now. In years we know shall come, who would have a moment to retrieve the lesser works? It's now the work is for, for what work can do now.

The last late question shrouds her like the smoke of earth on fire; actual soil so chemical it flares; the waves themselves are cresting flame, the sea in its black gown. Won't you lay me down and love me, won't you lay me down to sleep...

You should say 'perilous' but you haven't used that word not even once in this whole new millennium. Maybe it no longer needs be said because things have moved beyond the use of words.

(

Even you're just walking your dog, and she's a mix of larger breeds whose boundaries are a blur and there's a judgement out there actually against the mere fact of her being, which rides back onto you, a tut tut here, and a coarse look there, but let them keep the fear behind the curling of their lip, there's sheer joy in the co-existing done, the wolf delight in being near her, running, rest.

*You're going to reap just what you sow...**

Neither have you mouthed 'titration' since 1983, but the drip feed of decades is now a flood.

The woman up ahead of you is slowing on the path, her hands before her, central at the belly, either messaging or making ripe a blade, a firearm, she turns around and...

...The moon so bright it took away my eyes...

                               ...lines spooling on the wind...

          ...in another's head the space we never know...

together under sky

       between the rising waters and the empty out of

                              streets
                              the fire and wall
                              the border and
                              the woods

the glassy door in mind opened on

                    no yielded to

the milk pale morning

          rain down(y) on the air

dust on the played stop vinyl
how the house plants are no longer
dry
there's oil hot in the pan

)

say crevasse
                how deep
say cleft

sun wind sky
light in every light and living thing
every surface
shining

behold the body
of the pure occasion
waiting to be held
and held again

It is said there are flowers that bloom only once in a hundred years.
Why should there not be some that bloom once in a thousand, in ten
thousand years? Perhaps we never know about them simply because
*this 'once in a thousand years' has come today.*******

What survives of us is landfill.

The crisis has just passed.
Uh oh, here it comes again.*****

* Lou Reed, from 'Perfect Day'

** told by George Saunders: www.newyorker.com/books/page-turner/

a-letter-to-my-students-as-we-face-the-pandemic

*** Samuel Menashe, from 'Cargo', and from his obituary:

www.theguardian.com/books/2011/aug/26/samuel-menashe-obituary

**** Yevgeny Zamyatin, from *We*

***** John Ashbery, from 'Laughing Gravy'

(

Ahren Warner

–

from *All the Jacks*

I.

I am in Pa Tong, I think, or at least I have taken to referring to my immediate surroundings as Pa Tong, rather than Phuket, in the same way that I have taken to leaving the 7/11 from which I have purchased coconut water or cigarettes, with a hearty 'khob-kun-Ka'.

Each time I say this, I elongate the 'Ka' for what seems like an age, imitating what I think I hear Thai people say, but in a way that is – realistically – such a dreadful rendition that I can't help but suspect that I sound like a racist Brit imitating Yul Brynner in *The King and I*.

It does not matter to me that 'khob-kun-Ka' is a grammatical construction that designates me as female. I feel that the effort is enough, and that the trans girl serving me in the 7/11 is delighted enough by my well-meaning attempt at her language. Although, underneath her exuberant cheeriness, I am aware of the likelihood that she detests me.

)

Why am I here? That is a very *good* question. It is an *excellent* question with a very long answer that my therapist would have called *multidetermined*, meaning that the action in question has a multitude of causes, and to focus on one would be to commit an act of gross simplification.

For a variety of reasons – not least that I am dubious about the competence of my therapist – I am going to ignore his advice and simplify: I am here to document the social interactions of Westerners staying in one of the largest party hostels in Phuket. It is the same reason that I have been in Bangkok, in Koh Samui, Koh Pha Ngan and Krabi, and why I will soon find myself twerking a violently homophobic Welsh rugby player in a Chiang Mai nightclub.

Here, in Pa Tong, the hostel is more than a hostel. It is a *resort*. It is replete with a swimming pool, with multiple levels of dorms, with an outside bar and a selection of the very best inflatable pool animals. There is a wild cat that sits on one of the high, white walls and stares at me as I drunkenly purr down the phone to a woman in England that I cannot love.

In a late essay, the recently dead French poet Yves Bonnefoy writes that poetry

is a relation of the person to their environment that ensures a space in their consciousness for the needs and intuitions of the body as much as those of the mind: a living body, destined to die.[1]

Another old, French man – one that is still alive, if only just – has written of poetry, of the poem as a 'lawless proposition'. Alain Badiou has written that

what poetry forbids is discursive thought... presuming the existence of a thinking of the poem, or that the poem is itself a form of thought, this thought is inseparable from the sensible. It is a thought *that cannot be discerned or separated as a thought*. We could say that the poem is an unthinkable thought.[2]

There is an unfortunate romanticism to Badiou's description of poetry, a sense of the philosopher's reverence for an art he loves, but for which he, himself, has little aptitude. It is this same romanticism, the same wistfulness, that you can detect in so many great thinkers – in Derrida, in Heidegger and Kristeva – as they approach the work of art. It is, I suspect, also the pathos of the fact that 'thinking about' poetry is never the same thing as the 'thinking *of* poetry'.

Is it too soon to suggest that there is a sense in which the 'thinking about' a man stood in the middle of a bar with his cock and balls wilting on a ping-pong table is never the same kind of thinking as the act of dropping one's pants and splaying one's scrotum against a beer-puddled surface?

Perhaps it is too soon, or perhaps it is never the right moment to make that observation.

V.

Matilda(2) is naked. I am lodged between her thighs. I am making good on my promise of a second stint, after the first ended abruptly in the hostel pool as we absently rutted, our attentions directed more towards

(

)

the incredibly tall Thai prostitute that was shouting at Brody, the hostel manager, and refusing to return his passport and documents unless he paid for the services she claimed to have rendered him.

I have been told that the perpetual concern of the conscientious ethnographer is the risk of *going native*, and yet this is not what I am doing. I am, I would suggest, simply making space in my long, working day for the 'needs and intuitions' of my body,[3] 'a living body', as Yves Bonnefoy rather glumly reminds us, that is 'destined to die'.

If Alain Badiou describes the poem as a 'lawless proposition', a kind of thought that is 'unthinkable' outside of the poem, or the poetic, itself, Bonnefoy attributes a similar notion of the 'unthinkable' to the photograph. Writing of photographers such as Henri Cartier-Bresson and Gaspard-Félix Tournachon − known by his pseudonym, Nadar − Bonnefoy tells us:

> One can do no more than merely outline the history of photography if one does not recognise the importance of the inherently and wholly poetic decisions that... have attempted to give to being a new kind of foundation, even there where its thinking has been destroyed.[4]

For Bonnefoy, the 'unthinkable', the destruction of thought, that he locates within the photograph − or, indeed, within certain photographers' photographs − is a product of the *chance* that is inherent to the photographic image, that haunts the photograph on an *ontological* level. This relation between 'chance' and that which is 'unthinkable' is key to the argument that Bonnefoy advances in his *Poetry and Photography*, where he writes that: 'chance is active in the photographic image, it deflects the aim of what we call composition, if there is one, it presents things existing as such in an existence beyond that which is reducible to thought.'[5] It as an argument that is not unrelated to that advanced by the great German filmmaker Harun Farocki. In *Industry and Photography*, for example, Thomas Elsaesser has suggested that Farocki 'pursues photography's separation of reference and discourse, by proving this to be a separation of the subject as well as a separation within the subject itself'.[6] This is something we might return to later, but − of course − we might not.

Either way, in Bonnefoy's essay, the argument for the irreducible, innate existence of chance within the photograph is rather quaintly made via – amongst other things – the paintings of Lorenzo Lotto. As Bonnefoy writes:

In the image, in fact, there is no place for chance. That which might seem to signify it has been deftly arranged. The folds in the Virgin Mary's dress, on an altarpiece, the cat that seems there by chance in Lotto's *Recanati Annunciation*, are the products of urges, desires, inevitabilities inherent to the painter's fantasy. There is no chance within the field of the image. The throw of the dice has truly abolished it.[7]

In contrast, the photographic image, originally – in the times of Daguerre and Baudelaire – captured on a copper plate rather than on film or the digital CMOS sensor, maintains an irreducible aspect of chance, of the haphazard and the unintended:

if we reflect on what, necessarily, was going to appear on that small plate of copper: the cloth on a table, soon the clothes on a body would appear before our eyes, with their real pleats decided by the chance of their material, not the art of the painter. This person that one makes a portrait of has a way of holding their arms that can no longer be completely decided by the photographer, and thus chance appears... And, soon enough, a cat wanders into the field of the lens, a cat that the photographer had neither planned nor wanted, something that one cannot say of any painting, despite the suggestion of Lotto's *Annunciation*.[8]

)

And, for Bonnefoy, this operation of chance, of material and reality beyond intention, beyond the decidability of either photographer or audience, is also the insistence of matter, of the world and of reality beyond the control of the subject and, indeed, beyond the parameters of the thinkable, beyond the parameters – indeed – of critical discourse.

I roll slowly away from Matilda(2), sweating and breathless, and stand up to retrieve my underwear from the bed that belongs to Matilda(1),

(

a bed on which my boxer shorts had landed at some point in the Pornhub inspired performance of *intense attraction* that Matilda(2) and I had earlier enacted, and which I felt – even at the time – seemed a little *overly* dramatic.

Matilda(2) has closed her eyes and seems intent on sleeping in the dorm bed that had been assigned to me, leaving me to sleep in the dorm bed assigned to Matilda(2), itself rather uncomfortably close to the bed of Matilda(1).

'You are on the pill, aren't you?' I say to Matilda(2).
'We already discussed that,' comes her drowsy reply.

I cannot remember the discussion to which she refers, but – assuming that her earlier response must have been in the affirmative – I slump down onto the only free bed in the dorm, watching Matilda(1) snore and sputter and mumbling something unintelligible in her sleep, as a naked young man called Bret retrieves his right leg from underneath her and heads rather coyly for the door.

)

VI.

There is very little I can recall about the hours either side of the awful events that unfolded on the 18 June 2019, sometime between the hours of 1am and sunrise, on a beach – Haad Rin – situated on the south-east stump of the island of Koh Pha Ngan.

I recall, for example, a chance encounter with two tall, inebriated men called Benjamin and Braydon, some hours before I travelled via songthaew to Haad Rin. Braydon was playing pool at one of the three tables that were located between the hostel swimming pool and the bar. He seemed about as *all-American* as one could be, his rusty, sand-coloured hair cut into a nondescript mid-length style that would not look out of place behind a desk in Midtown or behind the counter of a Starbucks in Hagerstown, Maryland. He was skinny but athletic, with ginger stubble that was neither untidy nor obviously cultivated. He was, perhaps, a human embodiment of the kind of low-level pervasive Americanism that the rest of the world tolerates, and which some might call cultural hegemony, but which we are also grateful to for the provision of iPads and Taylor Swift.

Ostensibly, Braydon's *boy*, Benjamin, was also playing pool, although Benjamin seemed mainly to be oscillating between swaying absently against his pool cue and sudden spasms of energy in which he would launch himself at a gaggle of female bathers sipping drinks and throwing an inflatable ball in the swimming pool, jumping high into the air, his legs tucked into his chest as he landed with a crash and splash on his bottom, having cleared the female bathers by ever diminishing distances.

I took Braydon's obvious frustration at Benjamin's absences as an opportunity to take a break from my camera.

'Do you mind if I play?' I ventured, picking up the cue that Benjamin had dropped as he dashed once again for the pool.

'Not at all, bro.'

I cannot be certain that Braydon's accent was as devoid of character as it now seems, but I remember being completely unable to place him within the – admittedly sketchy – mental map of North American accents that I have assembled over the several years that I have been loitering in the party hostels of Europe and Asia.

The next hour or so would teach me that both Braydon and Benjamin had travelled from northern California, although Braydon had spent most of his adult life in Toronto. It would also provide irrefutable proof of something that I had long-suspected, namely that my pool skills increase in direct proportion to the amount of alcohol that I consume.

One thing led to another, or perhaps more accurately, one game of pool led to another, each accompanied by a strong drink, and with the taste of victory passed between us like the spit in the mouths of the two girls dramatically staging a French-kiss for the wonderstruck young men from Bolton who were also standing a metre or so away from us. At some point, Benjamin rejoined us, seemingly more in control of his limbs and libido and our attention and efforts became more intensely directed towards drinking, with both Braydon and I delegating our pool duties to two Thai infants that had been studiously watching us and lighting our cigarettes for the best part of an hour.

I had no interest in photographing the two girls kissing, although the expressions on the faces of the wonderstruck young men from Bolton were so exaggerated that I glanced towards my camera, thinking briefly (and, indeed, *pompously*) about the eyebrows and lower eyelids of an elderly Greek deity in a particularly gruesome painting by Peter Paul Rubens.

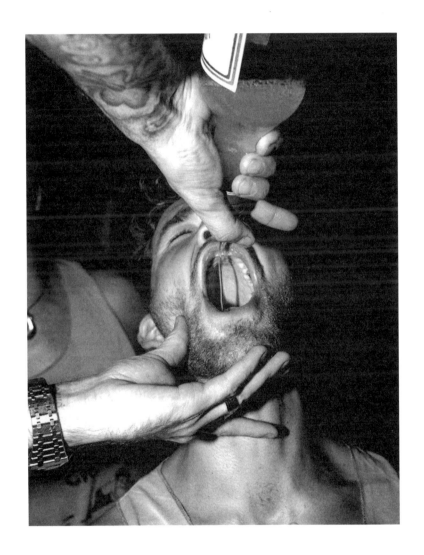

)

(

And yet, perhaps there might be something in this spectacle of two girls making out in order to... *what*?

To entertain, perhaps, or to *excite*, an assorted gaggle of early twenty-something men. And when I say that there is 'something in this', there are – of course – many *somethings* that one could examine: the weirdly unreconstructed, rather passé idea of feigned lesbianism as an erotic performance, the misogyny, the homophobia, the oddly old-fashioned persistence of such a pedestrian form of 'transgression'...

There is all of that, of course, but then there is also a way in which this phenomenon asks certain questions, or implies certain avenues for development, of Yves Bonnefoy's argument for the photographic image as the harbinger of radical chance within the regime of image-making.

Imagine then, a photograph of two girls kissing, with four or five topless young men watching, grinning and hollering. For Bonnefoy, of course, the point is that in the paintings of Lorrenzo Lotto (or of Rubens, in fact), 'there is no place for chance... that which might seem to signify it has been deftly arranged': the random or arbitrary is in fact the product 'of urges, desires, inevitabilities inherent to the painter's fantasy'. In one sense this is true, although perhaps it is an argument that leaves little room for a certain kind of transposed indexicality, wherein the 'folds in the Virgin Mary's dress' that one sees in a Lotto painting, are stolen from the chance folds of a draped model used in the production of the painting.

)

But here, photographing two girls making out, a gaggle of young men hollering, one might also say that there is – in a radically different way – 'no place for chance', or at least very little. The lie, of course, of the documentary photograph – even of the best, even of the most exceptional, the most sublime or horrific, whether of Mccullin, Doisneau, or Salgado – is that what they are presenting within the 'field of the image' is a chanced upon composition, and not – in a certain way – the product of a network of determinant 'urges, desires, inevitabilities'.

There is a way in which two rather drunk girls kiss, the way in which they make out as erotic performance, that is absolutely determined by a certain, culturally pervasive, kind of fantasy, desire and urges. Their limbs intertwine and their exaggerated gobbing moves to a rhythm determined by their own, necessarily fantastical, ideation of themselves as sexual beings, a sexuality internalised via the fantasies

149

of others. And here, in this space, in this party hostel in Koh Pha Ngan, one might, therefore, photograph what is at once both chance encounter and the culturally determined translation of fantasy, the performance of fantasy as ubiquitous, pre-packaged spectacle. A pre-packaged ubiquity – and here, perhaps, is the fundamental rupture that the critical register can never resolve – that is no less *authentic* in terms of its *affect* on our young, wonderstruck men from Bolton for the network of artificed cultural determination in which it is embedded.

I might, then, have decided to photograph these girls (or, more likely, their eager and hollering audience), if it wasn't for Braydon and Benjamin pulling me away from the bar and leading me down a gnarled trio of concrete steps to trudge the three-hundred metres of dirt path that led to the private twin room they occupied above a rather quaint rock 'n' roll bar in which an old Thai lady kept two menus. The first, of course, was written in chalk above the bar and was standard fare – mojito bucket, margarita bucket, long-island iced tea bucket – whilst the second came on a laminated A4 page that the barmaid kept under the bar and which offered a cornucopia of pharmaceutical delights, one which ran the entire gamut – marijuana, cocaine, LSD – and all marked up at eye-wateringly expensive tourist rates.

(

[1] Yves Bonnefoy, *Poetry and Photography* (Paris: Galilée, 2014), author's translation.

[2] Alain Badiou, *Handbook of Inaesthetics*, trans. Alberto Toscado (Stanford: Stanford University Press, 2005), 17.

[3] *lolz*

[4] Bonnefoy, *Poetry and Photography*.

[5] Ibid.

[6] <<https://www.harunfarocki.de/films/1970s/1979/industry-and-photography.html>>

[7] Bonnefoy, *Poetry and Photography*.

[8] Ibid.

)

Mira Mattar

—

Artists Open House: A Horror Story

The raindroplets on the Audis outside the semi-converted church glinted in the back of my eye. Kit Kat foil touching a filling. Visible from so many spots in Forest Hill, the intricate spire of the gothic Christ Church followed you round town – you go to Superdrug, you go to Sue Ryder, you walk in the Horniman Gardens. You could see it from all over the south London suburb, like John Smith's black tower, watching you.

There's a word for that molar metallic tang in Arabic, *lamse*. Touch, like a glance. How the lightest contact can announce something terrible. A tiny battery in your mouth. Ions carried through the saliva sparking when the two metals touch, a galvanic shock. Bilinguality can be a lonely terrain. You're always also having a second conversation just with yourself, in your other little heart. That kind of white metallic light rang out clinically, an immediate pain signalling potential more pain to come. That was the anxiety of being a child waiting in the dentist's office, or an adult waiting for a lover that just would not love, or in this case, two old friends sucking their Fruit Pastille lolly sticks and wondering where to maturely deposit them. One of them wanted to litter, the other disapproved. They decided together to stack the sticks against a bit of sticking-out church architecture. They were 36. This friendship flourished particularly well amidst the silliest challenges.

It was August. Hot. Actual hot like in real countries. It had been all summer. As usual this made the British nervous. Day after day. Swimming outside even. Walking home late with bare arms and that heavy blossom smell. Grinning. Woozy floral scents and ripe white t-shirts, pigeons ravaging leftovers from polystyrene takeaway boxes chucked, hot rubbish smell. Perhaps it was perversion but I liked it all. I liked how things couldn't hide – smells and needs, how the body was feeling, how wrong the world was, how we didn't have much time left. Just taking it easy with that sick gelatine creaminess inside bright red ice sugar lolly. Hyperventilating on the bus, a whole wet thigh up against yours. On your way to work. Stoned in a park, pissing in the

(

bushes, the possibility of somebody beautiful feeding you black-berries. The two friends, born a few months apart in 1983, one in London the other in Manchester – squalling curly heads, strange interiors – had lived close to each other, in Coventry accidentally, and on purpose in south east London, for 18 years.

That summer, I had recently been liberated against my will from a number of situations. This meant that on a Sunday morning I could do whatever I wanted. It was good to remember that freedom, that is, a *feeling* of it only (at this point in history), means losing something too. It kept hurting, but sometimes when there are no options the path becomes starkly clear – in that it is the only one. (Still, I hope you are never abandoned.) What I kept realising more and more and more was that freedom and happiness weren't the same thing, weren't even parallel lines. All this meant on that morning is that I could indulge my desire to see into the houses of others who had opened them up – for reasons probably ranging from narcissism to loneliness to a semblance of neighbourhood friendliness – in the name of Art, and in the name of Art's cousin, Community, under the friendly organisational umbrella of the Artists Open House. I didn't like to imagine all those dirty trainers in my narrow hallway, looking out the dirty windows, paying me compliments as I might see suddenly the dust for the first time in practically solidified lumps settled on top of every light switch. I love people, I love strangers even more sometimes, but not while I am enjoying the illusion of my home. Still, if ever there's a chance to see inside an unusual structure, I will take it. I'd identified my tendency to allow unmonitored, rudderless, curiosity to be a guiding principle – snorting up whatever comes my way then detailing the aftermath. I'd seen how it can erode me in a relentless insistence to strip away anything that wasn't the fact of mortality. So now I knew what degree of wanting to know wouldn't kill me dead.

Artists Open House it said with an arrow on an a4 sign and we followed. The apostrophe? I worried about possession again. Into the lift and up, out and along, a door open and no one there. This was the entrance to the spire. Almost the whole church was flats now, for people older and richer than us, and the spire, we presumed, must be the fanciest one. We looked at each other, sensing the beauty to

)

come, and readied ourselves to feel inadequate. Our little flats, with our little toasters, Ikea shelf inserts, teaspoons with nothing to say for themselves at all. To the right of the blasé hallway was a short flight of stairs, proper wood, from real tress, deep honey shine, like clear caramel. It was already delicious. The steps opened onto the second floor, a space defined by gorgeous wooden beamed vaulting, all in that honey coloured elastic ease, as if they weren't holding anything up at all. Nothing in the room save a dining table with fashionable perspex chairs – presumably to offset the traditional wooden table – and a what might be mistakenly called 'Moroccan'-style chaise longue, scattered with kilim cushions. A few more steps carried us up, ogling at the soft furnishings, to the kitchen, where we found the people.

A lithe, white-skinned woman, probably our age, sat very well with a balloon glass of red wine before her, and her two very clean, fair friends, also behind their big glasses. They were laughing but in a knowing way, like laughter during an emergency. She had smooth golden hair and a giant, very detailed artwork behind her. The window, which was the spire's clock, a disc rotating about its central axis, was open, letting in the day in stark pretty halves, and somehow in itself, alarming, that that could be done to a clock. Like the kitchen surfaces, it had a shining face, upon which the sun glared in flat, occasional flashes. We greeted the beautiful woman. I wanted to touch her skin. Are you The Artist we ask. She laughs, I used to be. My husband is upstairs, she gestures. There are no signs of children but I knew they were there for I could sense what they sense, the edges of this woman – angry, frayed, hiding. I know those edges from both sides. But it was hard to tell if I was really seeing and for the first time perceiving – or, if my own terror was casting everything I saw in the darkest shadows. But, just because I knew I was seeing through a symptom, it did not mean that I was not seeing clearly.

I didn't care about the art, I was there for the horror of property. And there was so much of it. We kept slipping up floor upon floor of caramel staired good taste in the narrowing spire, with only space for one room per floor. Sometimes there would be a bathroom, chic but usable; other times a child's bedroom with little curtains decorated in sweet primary coloured dinosaurs hiding stores of toys; innovative book storage techniques, things you'd never think up yourself; a bedroom of a teenager encouraged to express himself or, to express his parents' desire to project this idea; pretty clothes stored in a half-open secret cupboard; colourful light falling in patches around us, at our feet and faces, from the stained glass restored for the conversion, until finally we climbed the penultimate staircase and entered the studio.

A perfectly square room with windows on all four walls. Modern casings had been built onto the backs of the original lancet windows, through which you could see the spectacular views across the borough and beyond. The houses, tiny from this height, rows and rows of ordinary, painful lives; organised patches of green for sanctioned pleasure and rest; my own block on a hill to the east, its pale yellow concrete helping me spot it; blinding flashes from paddling pools; cats and their shadows stalking; schools; super-markets; the train station – its bridge under which the council would, two years later, paint over the graffiti commemorating the life and death of S, the woman who lived under that bridge for many years before her early passing. And The Artist there at his big tall table, a) black-and-white striped long sleeved t-shirt curving over his rounding belly, black baseball cap, white face. The images he made were large black-and-white linear designs of repeating patterns, reminiscent of Turkish carpets, or Levantine embroideries, but without depth or energy, without the history of black or white, without even the withoutness of nihilism, without Gothic romance, without the radicalism of Malevich, without without without, as if black took away instead of defined. He talked us through the black pens he used. Black Sharpies. Different nibs. He gets through so many black Sharpies. It's hard to work here because the kids are so noisy. He shows me a huge drawing, a white curve on a Sharpie black background. Above the curve, towards one of its edges is a white circle, below the curve is another curve, as the one that would be made by a thumb and an index finger working together to form a U shape. I step back a little and see ah – it's a hand cupping a breast.

A feeling I didn't recognise then but know now was curving into the lower part of my body. Just because something is boring it doesn't mean it isn't dangerous. As The Artist spoke excitedly with my friend about my friend's work, which was of interest to The Artist, the feeling snaked further in. The Artist's son, it turned out, might benefit from my friend's expertise and so was summoned with one clear call, not even very loud, and alarmingly potent. A teenage boy emerged, sweet, stuttering – something in his look that told me he was always doing his very, very best and yet. The Artist observed my friend speaking kindly with the boy. I tried to shift the focus so they could talk without observation. I sensed the boy performing, and in a deeper way than the one that sometimes occurs when a teenager speaks with an adult. The Artist wouldn't talk to me. Out of habit, and because I didn't want him to become interested in me, I had played myself down. Acting like you were boring was an increasingly helpful defence. I stepped back and let them talk and be watched. I took photographs of the views. You could stand in the middle of the room and turn around the spot and see the horizon in 360 degrees. Had I ever seen that before? Kent to one side and the City to another, swathes of suburb and green belt, simultaneously spacious and claustrophobic. I think to produce work in a room like this might impede it. What would detail mean after this? The son was excused and The Artist worked on my friend. Slick, falsely louche, about a decade our senior, lucked out on the property ladder and making a lot through advertising which funded the art – as though there were a difference. The room was so hot. All those windows, all that light. I didn't want to be closer to a bird than to a cat. You had to go through the studio to get to the master bedroom above. It was the only way. The beautiful wife had to come through this studio, these artworks, to sleep beside this man. Sometimes the worst part is how loud the same problem is.

(This story was shortlisted for the Desperate Literature Prize for Short Fiction 2020, for which *PROTOTYPE* was a partner journal.)

Mira Mattar

Oli Hazzard

—

from *Lorem Ipsum*

. . . I wondered if anyone had had the idea of designing some (impossible
buildings), which, of course, someone has, when I googled the phrase I came
across the website of the Catalan, Barcelona-based artist and photographer
I, of whom I'd never heard, but who has created, through a combination of
photography and 3D digital rendering, a series of hyper-realistic images
of buildings which it would be physically impossible to build in our world
('The techniques I use are often described as "camera matching" or "perspective matching" and several 3D software packages provide functionalities
that allow you to perform this,' he explained, but added that he tends to
do a lot of the work by hand to 'reach the level of detail needed to achieve
high photorealism'), at least at the moment, with engineering at its current
state of development (who knows, perhaps in forty years' time some new
material will have been discovered that will allow such structures to exist),
buildings like the oddly-titled 'Defence', which consists of a thin, shabby-
looking building which rises vertically about five floors, then from which a
much larger block juts out horizontally to the left for dozens of 'floors'
(though presumably 'floors' would be 'walls' in that horizontal arrangement),
a structure which in reality would, of course, be fatally unbalanced, a lesson
which I have been trying to impart to D, when we play with his Duplo, and
after a usually quite promising beginning to the process of constructing a
tower—a few blocks will clump together to form a rough base, and then an
erratic-looking vertebrae, constituted of horribly clashing colours, will start
developing upwards out of it, and becoming almost immediately unstable—
it will collapse unspectacularly, limply toppling, causing him to cry and
become confused and frustrated and angry, feelings which I will try to assuage or mollify by explaining that this event can be prevented from occurring
again (or can be made to occur much less frequently) by approaching the
task of construction in a more considered and systematic fashion, and as I'm
trying to explain this I will also be demonstrating physically how this should
be done, first creating a solid, wide, square base, and then building a narrower
tower on top of that (*look*, I say, *watch*) lacing together into a sturdy object
those bricks with six nodules or little circles on top so that forces which will
shortly test the integrity of the structure (gravity, his finger) will have a

)

greater chance of being absorbed or resisted by being distributed among the seams which both connect and divide the individual blocks, though as I explain this to him he refuses to be comforted, if anything my explanation makes him even more distressed and he begins to wail, which I find difficult to deal with because by this point I have become authentically absorbed in the task of assembling the tower, the activity has become wholly detached from the occasion or the need which gave rise to it, much in the way a poet, in an era long before our own entry into the world, would receive a stipend or a commission from a patron, and in agreeing to receive this fee the poet would commit themselves to paying tribute to the patron in some way in the artwork which the fee enabled (by clearing time for the poet to write poems rather than, presumably, just being destitute or having another job, such as barman, cook, scribe, or clerk, or lawyer, and so on, all of which activities would have diminished the amount of time for the poet to spend thinking about poetic things, though of course the activity of working in a field unrelated to poetry might itself prove equally if not more generative of poetry, depending on the sensibility of the poet), usually through a dedication at the front of the work, in which the patron would sometimes be addressed directly and praised lavishly for their beneficence, their accomplishments in the political world, the nobility of their family, their splendid house, and so on, and though many of these dedications or addresses to patrons are formulaic, and rehearse familiar tropes and employ routine image-sets, others, such as those by J, are obviously ironic, using these familiar tropes in such an exaggerated or histrionic manner that it becomes clear that the poet is lampooning the obligation to gratitude and subservience the poet-patron relationship has enforced upon them, though perhaps most interestingly there are occasional examples in which it becomes apparent, some distance into the dedicatory passage, that despite (or maybe because of) the murky or troubling or unstable circumstances of its composition the poet has become authentically absorbed in the activity of composing, so much so that a degree of imaginative detachment from the originating impulse for the work (whether accepted as a necessary part of the economy of poetic composition, or implicitly rejected as a 'corruption' or distortion of the artistic process, which presumably should occur as naturally as leaves to the tree) has been achieved, and that this originating context (or the pretence of one) has in fact entirely evaporated, or has become so obscured by the manoeuvrings of the poet's syntax, which have taken the poet so far into the poem (as though into the labyrinth, from which there seems no escape until it has been escaped) that they cannot see how it began and how it will end, though of course this is merely an unverifiable response I have experienced when reading such poems, and in fact I can imagine how the verisimilitude of the depiction of authentic absorption in the artistic act enabled by a financial transaction which is swiftly transcended might itself represent the most fawning of possible tributes (so gracious and enabling is the patron that they themselves have facilitated their own marginalisation in favour of the foregrounding of the artwork, and so on), especially since even in such instances it's at no point entirely clear who is speaking, the poet or the patron (is the former simply a mouthpiece for the latter, or the latter a platform for the former, and so on), or who is looking over whose shoulder—*who is looking over my shoulder*—or in what unstable compound these two figures or entities speak through one another, which is a predicament expressed almost constantly today in realms far beyond the act of poetic composition, such as on social media, where it seems that anyone who has a connection to an institution of any kind (or is employed in any capacity) supplies a caveat in their bio note stating that 'all views are my own' (when I see this phrase I tend to think of something my mother once said, when talking about an old boyfriend of hers from college, I think, who was a PhD student, and when I asked what a PhD was—I was maybe nine or ten at the time, though to be totally honest I didn't really know what a PhD was until my early twenties— she said that it was a qualification you received when you contributed an 'original thought' to the world, a nice definition, I think, but one which she delivered to me in a tone which conveyed an unstable compound of awe and contempt, as though she were so overwhelmed by the profundity of the idea of an original thought that she was suspicious of anyone who claimed to have had one (immediately after offering this definition, she said, 'I've never had an original thought in my life', again with an odd combination of resignation and delight, as though the inability to think anything original were a cause for both despair and celebration), an attitude which I must have absorbed in some distorted form, since shortly after that conversation I discovered the page on Ceefax (a text transmission system developed in the late 1960s by engineers at the BBC, originally intended to transmit a printable page of text during the nocturnal 'close-down' period of normal television transmission, but which rapidly developed into a sophisticated electronic 'site' operated with the remote control, which I used to watch live updates of football

)

scores on, the experiential analogy that first sprang to mind on the first day I used the Internet, that day so long ago) dedicated to the compilation of inspiring or insightful quotations or epigrams from philosophers and writers from throughout human history, and which I soon began dropping into conversation with my mother, without any kind of preamble or the slightest concern for their relevance to the conversation at hand, as though it were completely natural for a child of nine or ten to say *you know, mother, luck is what happens when preparation meets opportunity*, or *when I let go of what I am, I become what I might be*) a phrase which seems, oddly, to be both obviously untenable and a kind of humblebrag, in the sense that when a person asserts the expression of their 'own views' in a given situation, the inverse—the scene in which others' views are expressed by the mouth-piece of the person—becomes sharply imaginable, and it makes me wonder, perhaps unfairly, if there is some overlap between those who assert the own-ness of their own views within the private or social sphere (as social media presumably is, or was, I don't know) and the kind of person I have encountered many times in my life, who when in 'work mode' takes a visible and almost perverse pleasure in acting as a transparent medium for the intentions of the insti-

(tution they represent, like the traffic warden who, once he has started issuing a ticket, states with an expression that conveys an odd mixture of resignation and pleasure that *there's nothing I can do*, an attitude which is probably in part related to or drawn from or generated by the relief of not having to choose how to act (so many of us hate having to choose, especially when the choice has consequences in the real world, when it affects the experiences of others and knocks their lives off the course they would otherwise have taken, it's a terrible thing, in a way, the freedom to select between the few options placed in front of us (there are always only a few options, 1 to 5, even though in theory it seems like the options are limitless), between giving a ticket or not giving a ticket, between two homes or two jobs, between the few recipes we know how to cook for dinner, an abundance of narrative possibilities so abstract and rich and fertile-seeming that it's almost paralysing, so much so in fact that sometimes we would rather choose *not choosing* above making a choice—*no, I don't want it, take it away, it's tainted, I couldn't*—and the way we rationalise this withdrawal from choice is to believe that not choosing were somehow the ethical or responsible route to take, as though it were better to deny our own agency and let the 'fates' or the constellations or the I-Ching or the SatNav decide or for events to run their course and so on, rather than to take responsibility for the task, which confronts us hundreds of times every day, of choosing between possible presents and possible pasts and possible futures, fully in the knowledge that once each choice has been made it will not just alter irrevocably our lives and the lives of those who are entangled with our own, but that that moment will stay there, and part of us with it—the version of us that made the choice and experienced it—fixed and suspended in an ongoing present, forever, as K hypothesises, an unbearable pressure of responsibility which is perhaps the reason why we like to play at choosing, or I do, at least, some of my most pleasurable evenings in recent months have just been spent 'trying to choose' a film to watch on Netflix or Amazon Prime and failing to come to a decision, since in the very act of shuffling through the seemingly-infinite range of choices available, in postponing the act of decision-making, I have found myself experiencing something closer to the aesthetic experience I'm after than any experience offered to me by any actual film, which is, of course, an endless deferral of closure, an infinite postponement of the resolution of form, but as well as enjoying the postponement of decision when I'm in very similar if not exactly identical mood I also like to play at actually deciding, which is the activity offered by the Moral Machine, a website hosted and operated by a research group at MIT whose purpose is to develop through crowd-sourcing a picture of a general moral system to determine how self-driving cars should behave in moments of potentially fatal uncertainty, a site which offers a vast number of different traffic scenarios in a basic cartoonish simulation and asks the user to decide which figures to save and which to plough into—a man and a woman are both walking across zebra crossings, a baby in a pram and three cats are crossing a road, a pregnant woman and two young workers are crossing one side of the road and on the other is a roadblock which would surely kill the passenger of the self-driving car, and so on—and collates these human responses in order to develop a picture of what is considered a proper or at least intelligible moral response when these narrative possibilities arise in real life, in the coming future which cannot be very far away or perhaps has even arrived in some parts of the world already, in Silicon Valley, presumably (I should confess at this point that I don't actually know if Silicon Valley is a 'real' place or not, is it just a marketing phrase for an area that's not even a valley or is it really a valley, it's one of those places that I think I would be surprised to find out if it was the latter) in which self-driving cars have entered the bloodstream of our highways and

)

our backroads and our existing moral universe, this game of choosing is, like all voting, pitched ideally in terms of maintaining an individual's psychic equilibrium between inconsequentiality and consequentiality, in the sense that there remains the flickering possibility that the decision I input into the simulation will inform how a self-driving car in a San Francisco street in twenty years' time will steer, but that the decision is so infinitesimally small and insignificant in the larger scheme of assertions that I can assuage any anxieties I have about the rightness or correctness of my own intervention by persuading myself that it represents merely a dot in a pattern, a flake in a flurry, a pixel in the image of a culture, though I have reservations about this project, and not just about the traffic-scenario-simulation itself, since I find it hard to see how by offering a series of choices which have to be taken for the simulation to proceed, it can accurately account for the tendency of humans in times of crisis not to decide, simply not to act, to abstain, to post-pone recognition of the severity of the moment until the very fire touched them, as L writes, when, describing the Great Fire in 1666, he offers a scene in which people and animals behave in a fashion which has little to do with an intelligible moral system, 'everybody endeavouring to remove their goods, and flinging into the river or bringing them into lighters that lay off', and 'poor people staying in their houses as long as till the very fire touched them . . .

(

)

(

Astrid Alben is a poet, editor and translator. Her debut collection *Ai! Ai! Pianissimo* was published by Arc in 2011, introducing 'a new and original voice in English poetry, serious and uncompromising' (R.V. Bailey). Her 2nd collection, *Plainspeak*, was published in 2019 by Prototype. Alben is co-founder and artistic director of the arts and sciences initiative PARS; curator of site-specific events that are a mixture of theatre, art installation and scientific experiment; and editor of the *Findings on...* series published by Lars Müller Publications. She is a Rijksakademie van beeldende kunsten Fellow (2005–2008) and was awarded a Wellcome Trust Fellowship in 2013 for her pioneering work across the arts and sciences. She is a trustee of the Poetry Translation Centre and Poetry London. astridalben.com / @AstridAlben

Caroline Bergvall is a poet, artist and vocal performer. She works across art-forms, media, histories, languages. Her practice integrates many ways of working and of collaborating across disciplines. Outputs include books, performances, installations, audio-works, drawings, essays. Her current performance cycle *Sonic Atlas* includes various live works each exploring the thresholds between song, speech, breath, conversation and ambient sounds. Of which the outdoor sunrise performance *Ragadawn* and the discussion-soundwork *Conference of the Birds*. In preparation: *Night Refuge*. Her most recent book *Alisoun Sings* (2019) concludes a trilogy of poetic works exploring medieval and contemporary sources. It opened with the collection *Meddle English: New and Selected Texts*, and was followed by *Drift* (2014), which was awarded a Cholmondeley Award for Poetry (2017) and a Bernard Heidsieck Art Literary Prize by the Centre Pompidou (Paris, 2017). She was a Judith E Wilson Fellow in Poetry and Drama (Cambridge, 2014), Writer-in-Residence (Whitechapel Gallery, 2015), Collaborative Fellow (Chicago, 2016). Currently Visiting Professor in Medieval Studies, Kings College London.

)

Linda Black is a poet and visual artist. She won the New Writing Ventures Award for poetry, received a Poetry School scholarship and her pamphlet *The Beating of Wings* (Hearing Eye, 2006) was a PBS recommendation. Collections are *Slant* (2016), *Root* (2011) and *Inventory* (2008) – all with Shearsman Books. *The Son of a Shoemaker* (Hearing Eye, 2012), collaged prose-poems based on the early life of Hans Christian Andersen plus the author's illustrations, was the subject of a Poetry Society exhibition in 2013. She is editor of *Long Poem Magazine*.

Lochlan Bloom is a British novelist and short story writer. He is the author of the novel *The Wave* and the novellas *The Open Cage* and *Trade*. He has written for BBC Radio, *Philosophy Now*, Porcelain Film, *Slant Magazine*, *Litro*, IronBox Films, *The Metropolist*, *H+ Magazine*, *Palladium Magazine* and *Calliope*, the official publication of the Writers' Special Interest Group (SIG) of American Mensa, amongst others.

Iain Britton is an Aotearoa New Zealand poet and author of several collections of poetry. Recent poems have been published or are forthcoming in *Harvard Review*, *Poetry*, *The New York Times*, *Wild Court*, *New Humanist*, *The Scores*, *Stand*, *Agenda*, *The Fortnightly Review*, *Bath Magg* and *Poetry Wales*. *THE INTAGLIO POEMS* was published by Hesterglock Press in 2017.

Sam Buchan-Watts is the author of *Faber New Poets 15* and *Cloud Study* and co-editor, with Lavinia Singer, of *Try To Be Better* (Prototype, 2019). He is the recipient of an Eric Gregory Award (2016) and a Northern Writers' Award for Poetry (2019).

Hisham Bustani is an award-winning Jordanian author of five collections of short fiction and poetry. His work has been translated into several languages, with English-language translations appearing in journals including *The Kenyon Review*, *Black Warrior Review*, *The Poetry Review*, *Modern Poetry in Translation*, *World Literature Today* and *The Los Angeles Review of Books Quarterly*. His fiction has been collected in *The Best Asian Short Stories*, *The Ordinary Chaos of Being Human: Tales from Many Muslim Worlds* and *The Radiance of the Short Story: Fiction From Around the Globe*, among other anthologies. His book *The Perception of Meaning*

(Syracuse University Press, 2015) won the University of Arkansas Arabic Translation Award. Hisham is the Arabic fiction editor of the Amherst College-based literary review *The Common* and was the recipient of the Rockefeller Foundation's Bellagio Fellowship for Artists and Writers in 2017.

Theodoros Chiotis is the editor and translator of the anthology *Futures: Poetry of the Greek Crisis* (Penned in the Margins, 2015). Other publications include *Screen* (in collaboration with photographer Nikolas Ventourakis; Paper Tigers Books, 2017) and *limit.less: towards an assembly of the sick* (Litmus, 2017). His work has appeared in *Catechism*, *Litmus*, *Datableed*, *Forward Book of Poetry 2017*, *Adventures in Form*, *Austerity Measures*, *Shearsman*, *aglimpseof*, *Visual Verse*, *lyrikline* and *Otoliths*, amongst others. He has translated contemporary British and American poets into Greek and Aristophanes into English. He is a member of the editorial board of the Greek literary magazine *[φρμκ]* and contributing editor for *Hotel* magazine. His project Mutualised Archives, an ongoing performative interdisciplinary work, received

the Dot Award from the Institute for the Future of the Book and Bournemouth University; he has also been awarded a High Commendation from the Forward Prizes for Poetry in 2017.

Cathleen Allyn Conway is a creative writing PhD student at Goldsmiths. She is the author of *Static Cling* (Dancing Girl Press, 2012), *All the Twists of the Tongue* (Grey Book Press, 2018), and *American Ingénue* (Broken Sleep Books, 2021). Originally from Chicago, she lives in London with her partner and son. Find her on Twitter @CatAllynC.

)

Emily Critchley is the author of twelve poetry collections, including *Arrangements* (Shearsman Books, 2018) and *Ten Thousand Things* (Boiler House Press, 2017). She is Senior Lecturer in English and Creative Writing at the University of Greenwich and lives in London with her daughter. Her most recent manuscript, *Home*, is forthcoming with Prototype in 2021.

Claire Crowther has published four collections with Shearsman Books. Her most recent, *Solar Cruise*, is a Poetry Book Society Recommendation for Spring

2020. She is deputy editor of *Long Poem Magazine*.

Susannah Dickey is the author of *bloodthirsty for marriage* (Bad Betty Press, 2020) and *genuine human values* (The Lifeboat, 2018). Her debut novel, *Tennis Lessons*, has just been published by Doubleday.

Tim Dooley is a tutor for the Poetry School, a Visiting Lecturer at the University of Westminster and an arts mentor for the Koestler Trust. He was reviews and features editor of *Poetry London* between 2008 and 2018. His poetry collections include *The Interrupted Dream* (Anvil, 1985), *Tenderness* (Smith Doorstop, 2004) *Keeping Time* (Salt, 2008) and *Weemoed* (Eyewear, 2017). 'Diving into *The Waves*' is derived from improvisations on arbitrarily chosen sentences in Virginia Woolf's novel.

Olivia Douglass is the author of *Slow Tongue* (2018). Their published and produced works span the genres of poetry, verse/ lyrics essays, short fiction and live literature. Olivia's writing is based around their interest in race, sexuality and language.

Their live readings convene these textual explorations; each reading is rooted in the practice of rhythm and shared space as a continuation of ancestral storytelling. 'Body Whispers/Acts of Submission' was commissioned by the National Poetry Library as part of Poetry International Festival at the Southbank Centre. Instagram: @oliviaddouglass Twitter: @_oliviadouglass

Michael Egan is from Liverpool. His first collection, *Steak and Stations*, was published by Penned in the Margins. His first novel, *Circles a Clover*, will be published by Everything With Words in 2021. He is currently working on his second novel, *Northern Ashes*. He teaches English at a secondary school in Cheshire.

Gareth Evans is trying to catch up.

Aisha Farr is an artist and writer who lives and works in London.

Miruna Fulgeanu is a Romanian-born poet, translator and librarian living in London. She has recently completed an MA in Creative & Life Writing at Goldsmiths. Her work has appeared in *Poetry London* and *amberflora*.

Mark Goodwin is a poet-sound-artist who speaks and writes in various ways. He has published six full-length books and seven chapbooks with various poetry houses. Mark's poetry was included in *The Ground Aslant: An Anthology of Radical Landscape Poetry*, ed. Harriet Tarlo (Shearsman Books, 2011) and *The Footing*, ed. Brian Lewis (Longbarrow Press, 2013). Both his books with Longbarrow, *Steps* (2014) and *Rock as Gloss* (2018), were category finalists in the Banff Mountain Book Competition. *Portland: A Triptych*, a collaborative work with Tim Allen and Norman Jope, was published by KFS in 2018. His next book with Shearsman, *At*, is forthcoming. Mark lives on a narrowboat in Leicestershire. 'Warm Glow-Ball' was first published online by Leafe Press's *Litter* magazine in 2008.

Philip Hancock's collection *City Works Dept.* appeared in 2018 from CB Editions. *Jelly Baby*, a film-poem, screened at various film festivals and was published by Areté.

Oli Hazzard has written two books of poetry, *Between Two Windows* (Carcanet, 2012) and *Blotter* (Carcanet, 2018), a book of criticism, *The Minor Eras: John Ashbery and Anglo-American Exchange* (OUP, 2018), and a book of prose, *Lorem Ipsum*, which will be published by Prototype in 2021. He lives in Glasgow, and teaches at the University of St. Andrews.

Hoagy Houghton is an interdisciplinary artist based in London. His artwork is autobiographical, drawing on observations of the melancholy and humour in everyday life.

Dominic Jaeckle is an (occasional) writer, (weak) researcher and (amateur) editor. Jaeckle co-curates and collates the irregular magazine *Hotel* and runs a minor publisher called Tenement Press. His writings and editorial works have been published internationally.

)

Aaron Kent is a working-class poet and publisher born and raised in Cornwall. He runs Broken Sleep Books and has had several pamphlets released. J.H. Prynne called his poetry 'Unicorn flavoured' and how do you top that? You can find him on Twitter @GodzillaKent.

Caleb Klaces is the author of *Bottled Air* (2013), which won the Melita Hume Poetry Prize and an Eric Gregory Award, and two chapbooks, *All Safe All Well* (2011) and *Modern Version* (2018). His debut novel, *Fatherhood*, was published by Prototype in 2019 and longlisted for the Republic of Consciousness Prize. His second collection of poetry, *My Little Finger*, is forthcoming from Prototype in 2021.

Lotte L.S. is a poet living in Great Yarmouth, the furthest easterly outlier of England. She keeps an infrequent and informal newsletter, Shedonism.

Ali Lewis received an Eric Gregory Award in 2018, and his pamphlet *Hotel* (Verve) was published in 2020. He is assistant editor of *Poetry London*, a tutor at the Poetry School, and a Northern Bridge doctoral student at Durham University.

Jazmine Linklater has published the pamphlets *Toward Passion According* (Zarf, 2017) and *Découper, Coller* (Dock Road Press, 2018). She is a co-founder of the queer feminist reading series No Matter, in Manchester, and in 2018–19 was a Poetry London mentee with Vahni Capildeo. A third pamphlet, *Figure a Motion*,

is forthcoming from Guillemot Press in September 2020.

Rupert Loydell is Senior Lecturer in the School of Writing and Journalism at Falmouth University, a writer, editor and abstract artist. He is the author of *Dear Mary* (Shearsman Books, 2017) and *The Return of the Man Who Has Everything* (Shearsman Books, 2015); has edited anthologies such as *Yesterday's Music Today* (co-edited with Mike Ferguson; Knives Forks and Spoons Press, 2014), *Smartarse* (Knives Forks and Spoons Press, 2011), *From Hepworth's Garden Out* (Shearsman Books, 2010) and *Troubles Swapped for Something Fresh: Manifestos and Unmanifestos* (Salt, 2010). He has contributed creative and academic writing to *Punk & Post-Punk* (which he is on the editorial board of), *Journal of Writing and Creative Practice*, *Musicology Research*, *NAWE* journal, *New Writing*, *Axon*, *Text*, *English*, *Revenant*, *The Quint: an interdisciplinary journal from the north* and *Journal of Visual Art Practice*; and co-authored a chapter in *Brian Eno: Oblique Music* (Bloomsbury, 2017) and in *Critical Essays on Twin Peaks: The Return* (Palgrave Macmillan, 2019).

(

Alex MacDonald received an Eric Gregory Award in 2016. His pamphlet *Knowing This Has Changed My Ending* was published in 2018 by Offord Road Books. His next pamphlet, *Delicious All Day*, will be published in 2020 by Sad Press.

Helen Marten is an artist based in London. She studied at the Ruskin School of Fine Art, University of Oxford and Central St. Martins, London. In recent years she has presented solo exhibitions at the Serpentine Gallery, London; Fridericianum, Kassel; CCS Bard, Hessel Museum, New York; Kunsthalle Zürich and Palais de Tokyo, Paris, among others. She was included in the 55th and 56th International Venice Biennales and in 2016 won both the Turner Prize and the inaugural Hepworth Prize for Sculpture. Marten's work can be found in public collections including Tate Collection, London; Guggenheim Museum, New York; and The Museum of Modern Art, New York. She has forthcoming solo exhibitions at Castello di Rivoli, Turin and Kunsthaus Bregenz. Marten's artwork is collected in three recent monographs and she works with Sadie Coles HQ, London;

Greene Nafali, NYC, and König Galerie, Berlin. Her debut novel, *The Boiled in Between*, is forthcoming from Prototype in September 2020.

Mira Mattar is a writer, editor and tutor. She has recently had work published in *Tripwire*, *Zarf* and *Datableed*. She is also a contributing editor at *Mute / Metamute*. She lives in south east London. More of her work can be found at: her-moth.tumblr.com

Otis Mensah, self-proclaimed mum's house philosopher and rap psalmist, offers an alternative take on contemporary Hip-Hop and spoken-word. With endeavours to shed light on existential commonalities through vulnerable expression, Otis's work reads like a stream of consciousness, using aesthetic language to paint worlds of thought. 'As the first Hip-Hop artist to be awarded a poet laureate title in the UK, he wants to use the position to break down barriers, smash the stuffy stereotype, and remind people that poetry is meant to be for the people.' – *The Guardian*. Otis's debut collection, *Safe Metamorphosis*, was published by Prototype in June 2020.

)

Lucy Mercer lives in London. Her poems have been widely published in magazines such as *Poetry London*, *The Poetry Review* and *The White Review*, amongst others, as well as in anthologies such as *Spells: 21st Century Occult Poetry* (Ignota, 2018) and *Try To Be Better* (Prototype, 2019). She was awarded the inaugural *White Review* Poet's Prize.

Vanessa Onwuemezi was the winner of the 2019 *White Review* Short Story prize for 'At the Heart of Things', published in *The White Review 26*. In addition, she has had work published by *MIR Online* and The Literary Consultancy.

Sinae Park is an illustrator based in Norwich, UK. For the last few years, her work has been about food, taste, relationships, gestures and mental health.

Molly Ellen Pearson has an MA in Poetry from the University of East Anglia. Her debut pamphlet, *HYDRA*, will be published by Marble Poetry in 2020.

Meryl Pugh lives in East London and teaches for Morley College, the Poetry School and the University of East Anglia. Her first collection, *Natural Phenomena* (Penned in the Margins) was the Poetry Book Society Guest Choice for Spring 2018.

Elizabeth Reeder, originally from Chicago, now lives in Scotland. Her first novels, *Ramshackle* and *Fremont*, are both critically acclaimed. She writes fiction, narrative non-fiction and hybrid work that creates spaces between forms, subjects and disciplines. Her work explores identity, family, illness and grief, creativity and landscapes. Her next novel, *An Archive of Happiness*, will be published by Penned in the Margins (September 2020). She is a MacDowell Colony Fellow and a senior lecturer in Creative Writing at the University of Glasgow. *MICROBURSTS*, a collaborative work with Amanda Thomson, is forthcoming from Prototype in spring 2021. elizabethkreeder.com / @ekreeder

Leonie Rushforth has published poems in a number of magazines and journals over the years, most recently in *PROTOTYPE 1*. She lives in East London. Her first full collection is forthcoming from Prototype.

Lavinia Singer lives in London and is an editor of poetry at Faber. With Sam Buchan-Watts, she co-edited *Try To Be Better* (Prototype, 2019), a creative-critical engagement with W. S. Graham.

Maria Sledmere is a writer, critic and editor, completing a DFA in anthropocene aesthetics at the University of Glasgow. She works with SPAM Press and Dostoyevsky Wannabe and is a member of A+E Collective. Recent publications include *nature sounds without nature sounds* (Sad Press, 2019) and *infra•structure* (Broken Sleep Books, 2020), a collaboration with Katy Lewis Hood. She blogs at musingsbymaria.wordpress.com.

Maria Stadnicka is a writer, journalist and PhD researcher at UWE, Bristol, UK. She completed her MA in Creative and Critical Writing at the University of Gloucestershire. She has won twelve Romanian National Prizes for poetry and her work is published, among others, by *Dissident Voice*, *International Times*, *Social Alternatives*, *Tears in the Fence*, *TEXT*, *The Journal*, *The Moth* and *Shearsman*. She is the author of three poetry collections: *Somnia* (Knives, Forks and Spoons Press, 2020),

The Unmoving (Broken Sleep Books, 2018) and *Imperfect* (Yew Tree Press, 2017). Her next collection, *Buried Gods Metal Prophets*, is due out in early 2021 with Guillemot Press. Further information about her work, collaborations and reviews at www.mariastadnicka.com.

Maia Tabet is an Arabic-English literary translator living in Washington, DC. Her translations have been widely published in journals, literary reviews and other specialised publications, including *The Common*, *The Journal of Palestine Studies*, *Words Without Borders* and *Portal 9*. She is the translator of Sinan Antoon's *The Baghdad Eucharist* (Hoopoe Press, 2017); Elias Khoury's *White Masks* (Archipelago Books, 2010; MacLehose Press, 2013) and *Little Mountain* (Minnesota University Press, 1989; Carcanet, 1990; Picador, 2007); and the co-translator, with Michael K. Scott, of the winner of the 2010 International Prize for Arabic Fiction (IPAF) *Throwing Sparks* by Abdo Khal (Bloomsbury Qatar Foundation Publishing, 2012).

Amanda Thomson is a visual artist and writer who is also a lecturer at the Glasgow School

)

of Art. Her interdisciplinary work is often about notions of home, movements, migrations, landscapes and the natural world and how places come to be made, and she has exhibited nationally and internationally. She earned her doctorate in interdisciplinary arts practice, based around the landscapes and the forests of the North of Scotland, in 2013. She lives and works in Glasgow and in Strathspey and feels an inexorable pull to the north. Her first book, *A Scots Dictionary of Nature*, is published by Saraband Books. *MICROBURSTS*, a collaborative work with Elizabeth Reeder, is forthcoming from Prototype in spring 2021. passingplace.com

Donya Todd is an artist living on a farm in Cornwall. Her work is inspired by the magical, marvellous and macabre. donyatodd.com / @donyatodd

David Turner is the founding editor of the Lunar Poetry Podcasts series, has a City & Guilds certificate in Bench Joinery along with the accompanying scars, is known to the Bristol, Kristiansand and Southwark Community Mental Health Teams as a 'service user' and has represented Norway in snow sculpting competitions. Widely unpublished. Working class. Picket-line poet. lunarpoetrypodcasts.com / @Silent_Tongue

Lizzy Turner is a poet and artist living in London. Her work has appeared in various places online and in print. She is the host of 'a poem a week' podcast. @LizzyTurnerPoet

Sarah Tweed is a writer living and working in London. She was born in Co. Antrim, Northern Ireland.

Anne Vegter started her career as an author of children's books and fairy tales. In 1991 her first poetry collection *Het Veerde* (*It Bounce*) came out. In 1994 her erotic tales, *Ongekuiste versies* (*Filth*), were published. Vegter's work is characterised by an elastic style, playful yet enigmatic and disturbing. In 2013 she became the first female Poet Laureate of the Netherlands. Her collaboration with the Syrian poet-migrant Gayath Almadhoun resulted in apocalyptic war poetry: *Ik hier jij daar* (*I Here You There*). In 2008 and 2011 her poetry collections

Spamfigher and *Eiland berg gletsjer* (*Island Mountain Glacier*) were nominated for the VSB Poetry Prize. Vegter was awarded the Libris Woutertje Pieterseprijs, the Anna Blamanprijs, the Taalunie Toneelschrijprijs and the Awater Poetry Prize. She regularly works as a songwriter and performer, collaborating with composers and musicians. Since September 2019 Anne Vegter has been CEO of the Royal Academy of Arts in Amsterdam.

Ahren Warner is a poet, artist and critic. His latest book – a text and film work – *The sea is spread and cleaved and furled* was published by Prototype in 2020. Previous books include *Confer* (2011), *Pretty* (2013) and *Hello. Your promise has been extracted* (2017), a collection of poetry, lyric prose and photographs. His work has received awards including an Arts Foundation Fellowship, Eric Gregory Award and several Poetry Book Society Recommendations, whilst he has either exhibited or screened film-works or photography at venues including the Centro de Cultura Digital (Mexico City), EU National Institute of Cultures (Athens) and Great North Museum (Newcastle). A recent film-work, *I'm thinking*

what would sound sincere but also like, oh, that's super cute, has been selected for Bloomberg New Contemporaries 2020.

Oliver Zarandi is a writer and photographer. His first book, *Soft Fruit In The Sun*, was published in 2019 by Hexus Press. His writing has appeared in *Hotel*, *iD*, *The Quietus*, *Vol 1 Brooklyn*, *Hobart*, *The Nervous Breakdown*, *Fanzine*, *Little White Lies* and more. Follow him on Twitter at @zarandi and Instagram @ozrndi.

)

ISBN 978-1-913513-03-0

9 781913 513030 >